Prentice Hall Just-In-Time Program in Decision Science

COMPILED BY

DSCI 306
Statistical Data Analysis and Management Science
Carol Markowski
Old Dominion University

Director of Database Publishing: Michael Payne
Sponsoring Editor: Karen Usdan
Editorial Assistant: Catherine O'Keefe
Operations Manager: Eric M. Kenney
Marketing Manager: Annabel Cellini
Cover Designer: Kyra Riggie

Cover Image Courtesy of Stock Market Photo

This special edition published in cooperation with Pearson Custom Publishing.

The following pages constitute an extension of this copyright page.

Printed in the United States of America

10 9 8 7 6 5 4 3 2 1

Please visit our web site at www.pearsoncustom.com

ISBN 0536643717

Pearson
Custom
Publishing

Prentice Hall and Pearson Custom Publishing are pleased to offer the option of customizing the Prentice Hall Decision Science texts listed below. This custom program allows you to choose only those chapters you wish to use in your course—whether a number of chapters from *one* book or mixing and matching chapters from *several* books in the program—to create an efficient and cost-effective teaching tool for your course. For more information on the program, please visit our website at www.pearsoncustom.com.

Business Statistics

Statistics for Business and Economics, Eighth Edition and Seventh Edition,
By James T. McClave, P. George Benson, and Terry Sincich
Copyright © 2001, 1998 by Prentice-Hall, Inc.
A Pearson Education Company
Upper Saddle River, New Jersey 07458

Basic Business Statistics, Eighth Edition,
By Mark L. Berenson, and David M. Levine
Copyright © 2001 by Prentice-Hall, Inc.

Statistics for Managers Using Microsoft® Excel,
Second Edition,
By David M. Levine, Mark l. Berenson, and David Stephan
Copyright © 1999, 1997 by Prentice-Hall, Inc.

Business Statistics: A Decision-Making Approach,
Fifth Edition,
By David F. Groebner, Patrick W. Shannon, Phillip C. Fry, and Kent D. Smith
Copyright © 2001 by Prentice-Hall, Inc.

Statistics for Management, Seventh Edition,
By Richard I. Levin, and David S. Rubin
Copyright © 1998, 1994, 1991, 1988, 1985, 1982, 1978 by Prentice-Hall, Inc.

Statistics for Business and Economics, Fifth Edition,
By Paul Newbold, William L. Carlson, Betty M. Thorne
Copyright © 2003 by Prentice-Hall, Inc.

Business Statistics: A First Course,
By David Levine
Copyright © 2003 by Prentice-Hall, Inc.

Production/Operations Management

Operations Management, Sixth Edition and Fifth Edition,
By Jay Heizer, and Barry Render
Copyright © 2001, 1999, 1996 by Prentice-Hall, Inc.

Integrated Operations Management: Adding Value for Customers
By Mark D. Hanna, and W. Rocky Newman
Copyright © 2001 by Prentice-Hall, Inc.

Service Management and Operations, Second Edition,
By Cengiz Haksever, Barry Render, Roberta S. Russell, and Robert G. Murdick
Copyright © 2000, 1990 by Prentice-Hall, Inc.

Managing Quality: An Integrative Approach
By S. Thomas Foster
Copyright © 2001 by Prentice-Hall, Inc.

Introduction to Supply Chain Management
By Robert B. Handfield, and Ernest L. Nichols, Jr.
Copyright © 1999 by Prentice-Hall, Inc.

Project Management for Business and Technology: Principles and Practice, Second Edition,
By John M. Nicholas
Copyright © 2001 by Prentice-Hall, Inc.

Principles of Operations Management, Fourth Edition,
By Jay Heizer, and Barry Render
Copyright © 2001 by Prentice-Hall, Inc.

Operations Management, Third Edition
By Roberta Russell, and Bernard Taylor
Copyright © 2000 by Prentice-Hall, Inc.

Cases and Readings in Production and Operations Management,
By Joseph C. Latona, and Jay Nathan
Copyright © 1994 by Prentice-Hall, Inc.

Supply Chain Management: Strategy, Planning, and Operation
By Sunil Chopra, and Peter Meindl
Copyright © 2001 by Prentice-Hall, Inc.

Production/Operations Management (continued)

Plant and Service Tours in Operations Management, Fifth Edition
By Roger W. Schmenner
Copyright © 1998 by Prentice-Hall, Inc.

Managing Business Process Flows
By Ravi Anupindi, Sunil Chopra, Sudhakar D. Deshmukh, Jan A. Van Mieghem, and Eitan Zemel
Copyright © 1999 by Prentice-Hall, Inc.

Management Science/Operations Research

Decision Modeling with Microsoft® Excel, Sixth Edition,
By Jeffrey H. Moore, and Larry R. Weatherford
Copyright © 2001, 1998, 1993, 1991, 1987, 1984 by Prentice-Hall, Inc.

Introductory Management Science, Fifth Edition,
By G.D. Eppen, F.J. Gould, C.P. Schmidt, Jeffrey H. Moore, and Larry R. Weatherford
Copyright © 1998 by Prentice-Hall, Inc.

Introduction to Management Science, Sixth Edition,
By Bernard W. Taylor III
Copyright © 1999 by Prentice-Hall, Inc.

Cases and Readings in Management Science, Second Edition,
By Barry Render et al.
Copyright © 1992 by Prentice-Hall, Inc.

Quantitative Analysis for Management, Eighth Edition,
By Barry Render, and Ralph M. Stair, Jr.
Copyright © 2003, 2000 by Prentice-Hall, Inc.

Managerial Decision Modeling with Spreadsheets
By Barry Render, Ralph Stair, and Nagraj Balakrishnan
Copyright © 2003 by Prentice-Hall, Inc.

Contents

v

1

Linear Programming: Model Formulation and Graphical Solution

Model Formulation

A Maximization Model Example

Decision Variables • The Objective Function • Model Constraints

TIME OUT for George B. Dantzig

Graphical Solutions of Linear Programming Models

Graphical Solution of a Maximization Model • The Optimal Solution Point • The Solution Values • Slack Variables • Summary of the Graphical Solution Steps

Management Science Application: Operational Cost Control at Kellogg's

Management Science Application: Estimating Food Nutrient Values at Minnesota's Nutrition Coordinating Center

A Minimization Model Example

Decision Variables • The Objective Function • Model Constraints • Graphical Solution of a Minimization Model • Surplus Variables

Management Science Application: Chemical Production at Monsanto

Irregular Types of Linear Programming Problems

Multiple Optimal Solutions • An Infeasible Problem • An Unbounded Problem

Characteristics of Linear Programming Problems

Properties of Linear Programming Models

Summary · References · Example Problem Solutions · Problems · Case Problems

Objectives of a business frequently are to maximize profit or minimize cost.

Many major decisions faced by a manager of a business focus on the best way to achieve the objectives of the firm subject to the restrictions placed on the manager by the operating environment. These restrictions can take the form of limited resources, such as time, labor, energy, material, or money; or they can be in the form of restrictive guidelines, such as a recipe for making cereal or engineering specifications. One of the most frequent objectives of business firms is to gain the most profit possible or, in other words, to *maximize* profit. The objective of individual organizational units within a firm (such as a production or packaging department) is often to *minimize* cost. When a manager attempts to solve a general type of problem by seeking an objective that is subject to restrictions, the management science technique called *linear programming* is frequently used.

Linear programming is a model consisting of linear relationships representing a firm's decision(s) given an objective and resource constraints.

There are three steps in applying the linear programming technique. First, the problem must be identified as being solvable by linear programming. Second, the unstructured problem must be formulated as a mathematical model. Third, the model must be solved using established mathematical techniques. The linear programming technique derives its name from the fact that the functional relationships in the mathematical model are *linear* and the solution technique consists of predetermined mathematical steps, that is, a *program*. In this chapter we will concern ourselves with the formulation of the mathematical model that represents the problem, and then with solving this model using a graph.

Model Formulation

A linear programming model consists of certain common components and characteristics. The model components include decision variables, an objective function, and model constraints, which consist of decision variables and parameters. *Decision variables* are mathematical symbols that represent levels of activity by the firm. For example, an electrical manufacturing firm desires to produce x_1 radios, x_2 toasters, and x_3 clocks, where x_1, x_2, and x_3 are symbols representing unknown variable quantities of each item. The final values of x_1, x_2, and x_3, as determined by the firm, constitute a *decision* (e.g., the equation $x_1 = 100$ radios is a decision by the firm to produce 100 radios).

Decision variables are mathematical symbols representing levels of activity.

The *objective function* is a linear mathematical relationship that describes the objective of the firm in terms of the decision variables. The objective function always consists of either *maximizing* or *minimizing* some value (e.g., maximize the profit or minimize the cost of producing radios).

The objective function is a linear relationship reflecting the objective of an operation.

The *model constraints* are also linear relationships of the decision variables; they represent the restrictions placed on the firm by the operating environment. The restrictions can be in the form of limited resources or restrictive guidelines. For example, only 40 hours of labor may be available to produce radios during production. The actual numerical values in the objective function and the constraints, such as the 40 hours of available labor, are *parameters*.

A constraint is a linear relationship representing a restriction on decision making.

The next section presents an example of how a linear programming model is formulated. Although this example is simplified, it is realistic and represents the type of problem to which linear programming can be applied. In the example, the model components are distinctly identified and described. By carefully studying this example, you can become familiar with the process of formulating linear programming models.

A Maximization Model Example

The Beaver Creek Pottery Company is a small crafts operation run by a Native American tribal council. The company employs skilled artisans to produce clay bowls and mugs with authentic Native American designs and colors. The two primary resources used by the company are special pottery clay and skilled labor. Given these limited resources, the company desires to know how many bowls and mugs to produce each day in order to maximize profit. This is generally referred to as a *product mix* problem type.

The two products have the following resource requirements for production and profit per item produced (i.e., the model parameters).

	Resource Requirements		
Product	LABOR (HR/UNIT)	CLAY (LB/UNIT)	PROFIT ($/UNIT)
Bowl	1	4	40
Mug	2	3	50

A linear programming model consists of decision variables, an objective function, and constraints.

There are 40 hours of labor and 120 pounds of clay available each day for production. We will formulate this problem as a linear programming model by defining each component of the model separately and then combining the components into a single model.

Decision Variables

The decision confronting management in this problem is how many bowls and mugs to produce. The two decision variables represent the number of bowls and mugs to be produced on a daily basis. The quantities to be produced can be represented symbolically as

$$x_1 = \text{number of bowls to produce}$$
$$x_2 = \text{number of mugs to produce}$$

The Objective Function

The objective of the company is to maximize total profit. The company's profit is the sum of the individual profits gained from each bowl and mug. Profit derived from bowls is determined by multiplying the unit profit of each bowl, $40, by the number of bowls produced, x_1. Likewise, profit derived from mugs is derived from the unit profit of a mug, $50, multiplied by the number of mugs produced, x_2. Thus, total profit, which we will define symbolically as Z, can be expressed mathematically as $\$40x_1 + 50x_2$. By placing the term *maximize* in front of the profit function, we express the objective of the firm—to maximize total profit:

$$\text{maximize } Z = \$40x_1 + 50x_2$$
where
$$Z = \text{total profit per day}$$
$$\$40x_1 = \text{profit from bowls}$$
$$50x_2 = \text{profit from mugs}$$

Model Constraints

In this problem two resources are used for production—labor and clay—both of which are limited. Production of bowls and mugs requires both labor and clay. For each bowl produced, one hour of labor is required. Therefore, the labor used for the production of bowls is $1x_1$ hours. Similarly, each mug requires two hours of labor; thus, the labor used to produce mugs every day is $2x_2$ hours. The total labor used by the company is the sum of the individual amounts of labor used for each product,

$$1x_1 + 2x_2$$

However, the amount of labor represented by $1x_1 + 2x_2$ is limited to 40 hours per day; thus, the complete labor constraint is

$$1x_1 + 2x_2 \leq 40 \text{ hr}$$

The "less than or equal to" ($\leq$) inequality is employed instead of an equality ($=$) because the 40 hours of labor is a maximum limitation that *can be used*, not an amount that *must be used*. This constraint allows the company some flexibility; the company is not restricted to using exactly 40 hours but can use whatever amount is necessary to maximize profit, up to and including 40 hours. This means that it is possible to have idle, or excess, capacity (i.e., some of the 40 hours not used).

The constraint for clay is formulated in the same way as the labor constraint. Because each bowl requires 4 pounds of clay, the amount of clay used daily for the production of bowls is $4x_1$ pounds; and because each mug requires 3 pounds of clay, the amount of clay used daily for mugs is $3x_2$. Given that the amount of clay available for production each day is 120 pounds, the material constraint can be formulated as

$$4x_1 + 3x_2 \leq 120 \text{ lb}$$

A final restriction is that the number of bowls and mugs produced be either zero or a positive value, because it is impossible to produce negative items. These restrictions are referred to as *nonnegativity constraints* and are expressed mathematically as

Nonnegativity constraints restrict the decision variables to zero or positive values.

$$x_1 \geq 0, x_2 \geq 0$$

The complete linear programming model for this problem can now be summarized as follows:

$$\text{maximize } Z = \$40x_1 + 50x_2$$
$$\text{subject to}$$
$$1x1 + 2x2 \leq 40$$
$$4x_1 + 3x_2 \leq 120$$
$$x_1, x_2 \geq 0$$

The solution of this model will result in numerical values for x_1 and x_2 that will maximize total profit, Z. As *one possible* solution, consider $x_1 = 5$ bowls and $x_2 = 10$ mugs. First, we will substitute this hypothetical solution into each of the constraints in order to make sure that the solution does not require more resources than the constraints show are available.

$$1(5) + 2(10) \leq 40$$
$$25 \leq 40$$

and

$$4(5) + 3(10) \leq 120$$
$$50 \leq 120$$

*A **feasible solution** does not violate any of the constraints.*

Because neither one of the constraints is violated by this hypothetical solution, we say the solution is *feasible* (i.e., it is possible). Substituting these solution values in the objective function gives $Z = 40(5) + 50(10) = \$700$. However, for the time being we do not have any way of knowing if $\$700$ is the *maximum* profit.

Now consider a solution of $x_1 = 10$ bowls and $x_2 = 20$ mugs. This solution results in a profit of

$$Z = \$40(10) + 50(20)$$
$$= 400 + 1{,}000$$
$$= \$1{,}400$$

*An **infeasible solution** violates at least one of the constraints.*

Although this is certainly a better solution in terms of profit, it is *infeasible* (i.e., not possible) because it violates the resource constraint for labor.

$$1(10) + 2(20) \leq 40$$
$$50 \nleq 40$$

The solution to this problem must maximize profit without violating the constraints. The solution that achieves this objective is $x_1 = 24$ bowls and $x_2 = 8$ mugs, with a corresponding profit of $\$1{,}360$. The determination of this solution is shown using the graphical solution approach in the following section.

Graphical Solutions of Linear Programming Models

A graphical solution is limited to linear programming problems with only two decision variables.

Following the formulation of a mathematical model, the next stage in the application of linear programming to a decision-making problem is to find the solution of the model. A common solution approach is to solve algebraically the set of mathematical relationships that form the model either manually or using a computer program, thus determining the values for the decision variables. However, because the relationships are *linear*, some models and solutions can be illustrated *graphically*.

The graphical method is realistically limited to models with only two decision variables, which can be represented on a graph of two dimensions. Models with three decision variables can be graphed in three dimensions, but the process is quite cumbersome, and models of four or more decision variables cannot be graphed at all.

The graphical method provides a picture of how a solution is obtained for a linear programming problem.

Although the graphical method is limited as a solution approach, it is very useful at this point in our presentation of linear programming in that it gives a "picture" of how a solution is derived. Graphs can provide a clearer understanding of how the computer and mathematical solution approaches presented in subsequent chapters work and, thus, a better understanding of the solutions.

Graphical Solution of a Maximization Model

The product mix model will be used to demonstrate the graphical interpretation of a linear programming problem. Recall that the problem described the Beaver Creek Pottery Company's attempt to decide how many bowls and mugs to produce daily, given limited amounts of labor and clay. The complete linear programming model was formulated as

maximize $Z = \$40x_1 + 50x_2$
subject to
$$x_1 + 2x_2 \leq 40 \text{ hr of labor}$$
$$4x_1 + 3x_2 \leq 120 \text{ lb of clay}$$
$$x_1, x_2 \geq 0$$

Management Science Application

Operational Cost Control at Kellogg's

Kellogg's is the world's largest cereal producer and a leading producer of convenience foods with worldwide sales in 1999 of almost $7 billion. The company started with a single product, Kellogg's Corn Flakes, in 1906 and over the years developed a product line of other cereals including Rice Krispies and Corn Pops, and convenience foods such as Pop-Tarts and Nutri-Grain cereal bars. Kellogg's operates 5 plants in the United States and Canada and 7 distribution centers, and it contracts with 15 co-packers to produce or pack some of Kellogg's products. Kellogg's must coordinate the production, packaging, inventory, and distribution of roughly 80 cereal products alone at these various facilities.

For more than a decade Kellogg's has been using a large-scale linear programming model called the Kellogg Planning System (KPS) to plan its weekly production, inventory, and distribution decisions. The model decision variables include the amount of each product produced in a production process at each plant, the units of product packaged, the amount of inventory held, and the shipments of products to other plants and distribution centers. Model constraints include production processing time, packaging capacity, balancing constraints that make sure that all products produced are also packaged during the week, inventory balancing constraints, and inventory safety stock requirements. The model objective is cost minimization. Kellogg's has also developed a tactical version of this basic operational linear programming model for long-range planning for 12 to 24 months into the future. The KPS model is credited with saving Kellogg's $4.5 million in reduced production, inventory, and distribution costs in 1995,

Photo courtesy of CORBIS BETTMAN

and it is estimated that KPS has saved Kellogg's many more millions of dollars since the mid-1990s. The tactical version of KPS recently helped the company consolidate production capacity with estimated projected savings of almost $40 million.

Source: G. Brown, J. Keegan, B. Vigus, and K. Wood, "The Kellogg Company Optimizes Production, Inventory, and Distribution," *Interfaces* 31, no. 6 (November–December 2001): 1–15.

where
x_1 = number of bowls produced
x_2 = number of mugs produced

Figure 1 is a set of coordinates for the decision variables x_1 and x_2, on which the graph of our model will be drawn. Note that only the positive quadrant is drawn (i.e., the quadrant where x_1 and x_2 will always be positive) because of the nonnegativity constraints, $x_1 \geq 0$ and $x_2 \geq 0$.

Constraint lines are plotted as equations.

The first step in drawing the graph of the model is to plot the constraints on the graph. This is done by treating both constraints as equations (or straight lines) and plotting each line on the graph. Consider the labor constraint line first:

$$x_1 + 2x_2 = 40$$

A simple procedure for plotting this line is to determine two points that are on the line and then draw a straight line through the points. One point can be found by letting $x_1 = 0$ and solving for x_2:

$$(0) + 2x_2 = 40$$
$$x_2 = 20$$

Figure 1

Coordinates for graphical analysis

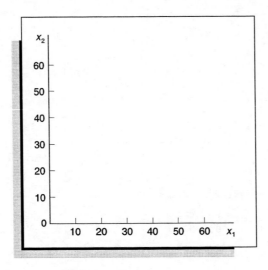

Thus, one point is at the coordinates $x_1 = 0$ and $x_2 = 20$. A second point can be found by letting $x_2 = 0$ and solving for x_1:

$$x_1 + 2(0) = 40$$
$$x_1 = 40$$

Now we have a second point, $x_1 = 40$, $x_2 = 0$. The line on the graph representing this equation is drawn by connecting these two points, as shown in Figure 2. However, this is only the graph of the constraint *line* and does not reflect the entire constraint, which also includes the values that are less than or equal to ($\leq$) this line. The *area* representing the entire constraint is shown in Figure 3.

Figure 2

Graph of the labor constraint line

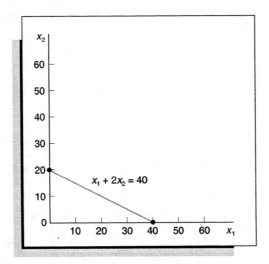

To test the correctness of the constraint area, check any two points—one inside the constraint area and one outside. For example, check point *A* in Figure 3, which is at the intersection of $x_1 = 10$ and $x_2 = 10$. Substituting these values into the following labor constraint,

Figure 3

The labor constraint area

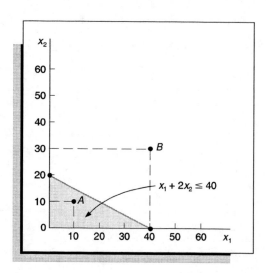

$$10 + 2(10) \leq 40$$
$$30 \leq 40 \text{ hr}$$

shows that point A is indeed within the constraint area, as these values for x_1 and x_2 yield a quantity that does not exceed the limit of 40 hours. Next, check point B at $x_1 = 40$ and $x_2 = 30$.

$$40 + 2(30) \leq 40$$
$$100 \nleq 40 \text{ hr}$$

Point B is obviously outside the constraint area, as the values for x_1 and x_2 yield a quantity (100) that exceeds the limit of 40 hours.

The line for the clay constraint is drawn in the same way as the one for the labor constraint—by finding two points on the constraint line and connecting them with a straight line. First, let $x_1 = 0$ and solve for x_2.

$$4(0) + 3x_2 = 120$$
$$x_2 = 40$$

Performing this operation results in a point, $x_1 = 0$, $x_2 = 40$. Next, let $x_2 = 0$ and then solve for x_1.

$$4x_1 + 3(0) = 120$$
$$x_1 = 30$$

This operation yields a second point, $x_1 = 30$, $x_2 = 0$. Plotting these points on the graph and connecting them with a line gives the constraint line and area for clay, as shown in Figure 4.

Combining the two individual graphs for both labor and clay (Figures 3 and 4) produces a graph of the model constraints, as shown in Figure 5. The shaded area in Figure 5 is the area that is common to both model constraints. Therefore, this is the only area on the graph that contains points (i.e., values for x_1 and x_2) that will satisfy both constraints simultaneously. For example, consider the points R, S, and T in Figure 6. Point R satisfies both constraints; thus, we say it is a *feasible* solution point. Point S satisfies the clay constraint ($4x_1 + 3x_2 \leq 120$) but exceeds the labor constraint; thus, it is infeasible. Point T satisfies neither constraint; thus, it is also infeasible.

Figure 4

The constraint area for clay

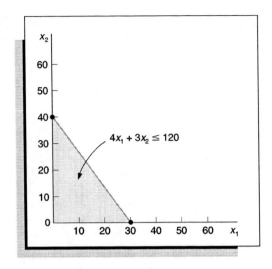

$4x_1 + 3x_2 \leq 120$

Figure 5

Graph of both model constraints

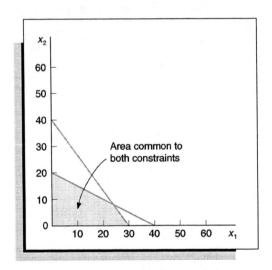

Area common to both constraints

*The **feasible solution area** is an area on the graph bounded by the constraint equations.*

The shaded area in Figure 6 is referred to as the *feasible solution area*, because all the points in this area satisfy both constraints. Some point within this feasible solution area will result in *maximum profit* for the Beaver Creek Pottery Company. The next step in the graphical solution approach is to locate this point.

The Optimal Solution Point

The second step in the graphical solution method is to locate the point in the feasible solution area that will result in the greatest total profit. To begin the solution analysis, we will first plot the objective function line for an *arbitrarily* selected level of profit. For example, if profit, Z, is $800, the objective function is

$$\$800 = 40x_1 + 50x_2$$

Plotting this line just as we plotted the constraint lines results in the graph shown in Figure 7. Every point on this line is in the feasible solution area and will result in a profit of

Figure 6

The feasible solution area constraints

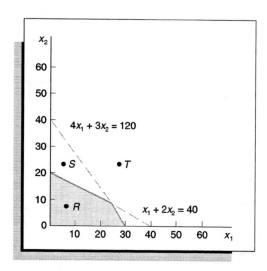

$800 (i.e., every combination of x_1 and x_2 on this line will give a Z value of $800). However, let us see whether an even greater profit will still provide a feasible solution. For example, consider profits of $1,200 and $1,600, as shown in Figure 8.

Figure 7

Objective function line for $Z = \$800$

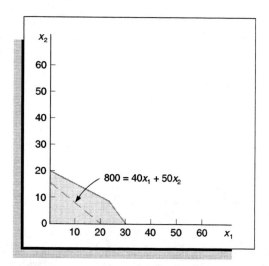

A portion of the objective function line for a profit of $1,200 is outside the feasible solution area, but part of the line remains within the feasible area. Therefore, this profit line indicates that there are feasible solution points that give a profit greater than $800. Now let us increase profit again, to $1,600. This profit line, also shown in Figure 8, is completely outside the feasible solution area. The fact that no points on this line are feasible indicates that a profit of $1,600 is not possible.

Because a profit of $1,600 is too great for the constraint limitations, as shown in Figure 8, the question of the maximum profit value remains. We can see from Figure 8 that profit increases as the objective function line moves away from the origin (i.e., the point $x_1 = 0$, $x_2 = 0$). Given this characteristic, the maximum profit will be attained at the point where the objective function line is farthest from the origin *and* is still touching a point in the feasible solution area. This point is shown as point B in Figure 9.

Figure 8

Alternative objective function lines for profits, Z, of $800, $1,200, and $1,600

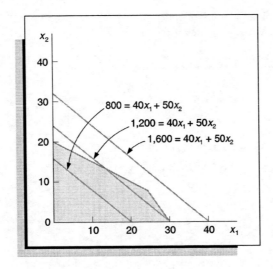

$800 = 40x_1 + 50x_2$

$1,200 = 40x_1 + 50x_2$

$1,600 = 40x_1 + 50x_2$

Figure 9

Identification of optimal solution point

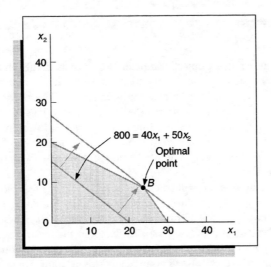

$800 = 40x_1 + 50x_2$

Optimal point

B

To find point B, place a straightedge parallel to the objective function line $800 = 40x_1 + 50x_2$ in Figure 9 and move it outward from the origin as far as you can without losing contact with the feasible solution area. Point B is referred to as the *optimal* (i.e., best) *solution.*

The **optimal solution** *is the best feasible solution.*

The Solution Values

The third step in the graphical solution approach is to solve for the values of x_1 and x_2 once the optimal solution point has been found. It is possible to determine the x_1 and x_2 coordinates of point B in Figure 9 directly from the graph, as shown in Figure 10. The graphical coordinates corresponding to point B in Figure 10 are $x_1 = 24$ and $x_2 = 8$. This is the optimal solution for the decision variables in the problem. However, unless an absolutely accurate graph is drawn, it is frequently difficult to determine the correct solution directly from the graph. A more exact approach is to determine the solution values mathematically once the optimal point on the graph has been determined. The mathematical approach for determining the solution is described in the following pages. First, however, we will consider a few characteristics of the solution.

Figure 10
Optimal solution coordinates

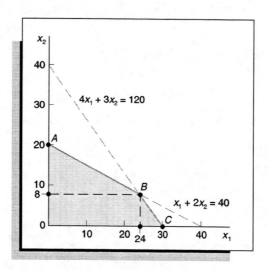

The optimal solution point is the last point the objective function touches as it leaves the feasible solution area.

In Figure 9, as the objective function was increased, the last point it touched in the feasible solution area was on the boundary of the feasible solution area. The solution point is always on this boundary, because the boundary contains the points farthest from the origin (i.e., the points corresponding to the greatest profit). This characteristic of linear programming problems reduces the number of possible solution points considerably, from all points in the solution area to just those points on the boundary. However, the number of possible solution points is reduced even more by another characteristic of linear programming problems.

The solution point will be on the boundary of the feasible solution area and at one of the *corners* of the boundary where two constraint lines intersect. (The graphical axes, you will recall, are also constraints, because $x_1 \geq 0$ and $x_2 \geq 0$.) These corners (points A, B, and C in Figure 10) are protrusions, or *extremes*, in the feasible solution area; they are called

Extreme points are corner points on the boundary of the feasible solution area.

extreme points. It has been proven mathematically that the optimal solution in a linear programming model will always occur at an extreme point. Therefore, in our example problem the possible solution points are limited to the three extreme points, A, B, and C. The optimal extreme point is the extreme point the objective function touches last as it leaves the feasible solution area, as shown in Figure 9.

Constraint equations are solved simultaneously at the optimal extreme point to determine the variable solution values.

From the graph shown in Figure 9, we know that the optimal solution point is B. Because point B is formed by the intersection of two constraint lines as shown in Figure 10, these two lines are *equal* at point B. Thus, the values of x_1 and x_2 at that intersection can be found by solving the two equations *simultaneously*.

First, convert both equations to functions of x_1:

$$x_1 + 2x_2 = 40$$
$$x_1 = 40 - 2x_2$$

and

$$4x_1 + 3x_2 = 120$$
$$4x_1 = 120 - 3x_2$$
$$x_1 = 30 - (3x_2/4)$$

Now let x_1 in the first equation equal x_1 in the second equation,

$$40 - 2x_2 = 30 - (3x_2/4)$$

and solve for x_2:

$$5x_2/4 = 10$$
$$x_2 = 8$$

Substituting $x_2 = 8$ into either one of the original equations gives a value for x_1:

$$x_1 = 40 - 2x_2$$
$$x_1 = 40 - 2(8)$$
$$= 24$$

Thus, the optimal solution at point B in Figure 10 is $x_1 = 24$ and $x_2 = 8$. Substituting these values into the objective function gives the maximum profit,

$$Z = \$40x_1 + 50x_2$$
$$Z = \$40(24) + 50(8)$$
$$= \$1,360$$

In terms of the original problem, the solution indicates that if the pottery company produces 24 bowls and 8 mugs, it will receive $1,360, the maximum daily profit possible (given the resource constraints).

Given that the optimal solution will be at one of the extreme corner points, A, B, or C, you can find the solution by testing each of the three points to see which results in the greatest profit, rather than by graphing the objective function and seeing which point it last touches as it moves out of the feasible solution area. Figure 11 shows the solution values for all three points, A, B, and C, and the amount of profit, Z, at each point.

Figure 11

Solutions at all corner points

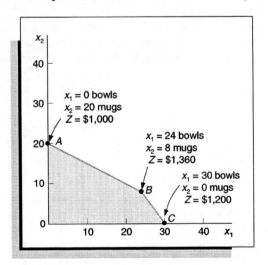

As indicated in the discussion of Figure 9, point B is the optimal solution point because it is the last point the objective function touches before it leaves the solution area. In other words, the objective function determines which extreme point is optimal. This is because the objective function designates the profit that will accrue from each combination of x_1 and x_2 values at the extreme points. If the objective function had had different coefficients (i.e., different x_1 and x_2 profit values), one of the extreme points other than B might have been optimal.

Assume for a moment that the profit for a bowl is \$70 instead of \$40, and the profit for a mug is \$20 instead of \$50. These values result in a new objective function, $Z = \$70x_1 + 20x_2$. If the model constraints for labor or clay are not changed, the feasible solution area remains the same, as shown in Figure 12. However, the location of the objective function in Figure 12 is different from that of the original objective function in Figure 9. The reason for this change is that the new profit coefficients give the linear objective function a new *slope*.

Figure 12

The optimal solution with
$Z = 70x_1 + 20x_2$

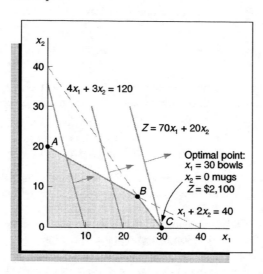

The slope is computed as the "rise" over the "run."

The slope can be determined by transforming the objective function into the general equation for a straight line, $y = a + bx$, where y is the dependent variable, a is the y intercept, b is the slope, and x is the independent variable. For our example objective function, x_2 is the dependent variable corresponding to y (i.e., it is on the vertical axis), and x_1 is the independent variable. Thus, the objective function can be transformed into the general equation of a line as follows:

$$Z = 70x_1 + 20x_2$$
$$20x_2 = Z - 70x_1$$
$$x_2 = \frac{Z}{20} - \frac{7}{2}x_1$$
$$\uparrow \qquad \uparrow \quad \uparrow$$
$$y \qquad a \quad\; b$$

This transformation identifies the slope of the new objective function as $-7/2$ (the minus sign indicates that the line slopes downward). In contrast, the slope of the original objective function was $-4/5$.

If we move this new objective function out through the feasible solution area, the last extreme point it touches is point C. Simultaneously solving the constraint lines at point C results in the following solution:

$$x_1 = 30$$
$$4x_1 + 3x_2 = 120$$

and

$$x_2 = 40 - (4x_1/3)$$
$$x_2 = 40 - 4(30)/3$$
$$x_2 = 0$$

Thus, the optimal solution at point C in Figure 12 is $x_1 = 30$ bowls, $x_2 = 0$ mugs, and $Z = \$2,100$ profit. Altering the objective function coefficients results in a new solution.

This brief example of the effects of altering the objective function highlights two useful points. First, the optimal extreme point is determined by the objective function, and an extreme point on one axis of the graph is as likely to be the optimal solution as is an extreme point on a different axis. Second, the solution is sensitive to the values of the coefficients in the objective function. If the objective function coefficients are changed, as in our example, the solution may change. Likewise, if the constraint coefficients are changed, the solution space and solution points may change also. This information can be of consequence to the decision maker trying to determine how much of a product to produce. *Sensitivity analysis*—the use of linear programming to evaluate the effects of changes in model parameters—is discussed in another chapter.

Sensitivity analysis *is used to analyze changes in model parameters.*

It should be noted that some problems do not have a single extreme point solution. For example, when the objective function line parallels one of the constraint lines, an entire line segment is bounded by two adjacent corner points that are optimal; there is no single extreme point on the objective function line. In this situation there are *multiple optimal solutions*. This and other irregular types of solution outcomes in linear programming are discussed at the end of this chapter.

Multiple optimal solutions *can occur when the objective function is parallel to a constraint line.*

Slack Variables

Once the optimal solution was found at point B in Figure 11, simultaneous equations were solved to determine the values of x_1 and x_2. Recall that the solution occurs at an extreme point where constraint equation lines intersect with each other or with the axis. Thus, the model constraints are considered as *equations* ($=$), rather than $\leq$ or $\geq$ inequalities.

There is a standard procedure for transforming $\leq$ inequality constraints into equations. This transformation is achieved by adding a new variable, called a *slack variable*, to each constraint. For the pottery company example, the model constraints are

A slack variable is added to a $\leq$ constraint to convert it to an equation ($=$).

$$x_1 + 2x_2 \leq 40 \text{ hr of labor}$$
$$4x_1 + 3x_2 \leq 120 \text{ lb of clay}$$

The addition of a unique slack variable, s_1, to the labor constraint and s_2 to the constraint for clay results in the following equations:

$$x_1 + 2x_2 + s_1 = 40 \text{ hr of labor}$$
$$4x_1 + 3x_2 + s_2 = 120 \text{ lb of clay}$$

The slack variables in these equations, s_1 and s_2, will take on any value necessary to make the left-hand side of the equation equal to the right-hand side. For example, consider a hypothetical solution of $x_1 = 5$ and $x_2 = 10$. Substituting these values into the foregoing equations yields

$$x_1 + 2x_2 + s_1 = 40 \text{ hr of labor}$$
$$5 + 2(10) + s_1 = 40 \text{ hr of labor}$$
$$s_1 = 15 \text{ hr of labor}$$

and

$$4x_1 + 3x_2 + s_2 = 120 \text{ lb of clay}$$
$$4(5) + 3(10) + s_2 = 120 \text{ lb of clay}$$
$$s_2 = 70 \text{ lb of clay}$$

In this example, $x_1 = 5$ bowls and $x_2 = 10$ mugs represent a solution that does not make use of the total available amount of labor and clay. In the labor constraint, 5 bowls and 10 mugs require only 25 hours of labor. This leaves 15 hours that are not used. Thus, s_1 represents the amount of *unused* labor, or slack.

In the clay constraint, 5 bowls and 10 mugs require only 50 pounds of clay. This leaves 70 pounds of clay unused. Thus, s_2 represents the amount of *unused* clay. In general, slack variables represent the amount of *unused resources*.

*A **slack variable** represents unused resources.*

The ultimate instance of unused resources occurs at the origin, where $x_1 = 0$ and $x_2 = 0$. Substituting these values into the equations yields

$$x_1 + 2x_2 + s_1 = 40$$
$$0 + 2(0) + s_1 = 40$$
$$s_1 = 40 \text{ hr of labor}$$

and

$$4x_1 + 3x_2 + s_2 = 120$$
$$4(0) + 3(0) + s_2 = 120$$
$$s_2 = 120 \text{ lb of clay}$$

Because no production takes place at the origin, all of the resources are unused; thus, the slack variables equal the total available amounts of each resource: $s_1 = 40$ hours of labor and $s_2 = 120$ pounds of clay.

What is the effect of these new slack variables on the objective function? The objective function for our example represents the profit gained from the production of bowls and mugs,

$$Z = \$40x_1 + \$50x_2$$

The coefficient \$40 is the contribution to profit of each bowl; \$50 is the contribution to profit of each mug. What, then, do the slack variables s_1 and s_2 contribute? They contribute *nothing* to profit because they represent unused resources. Profit is made only after the resources are put to use in making bowls and mugs. Using slack variables, we can write the objective function as

A slack variable contributes nothing to the objective function value.

$$\text{maximize } Z = \$40x_1 + \$50x_2 + 0s_1 + 0s_2$$

As in the case of decision variables (x_1 and x_2), slack variables can have only nonnegative values, because negative resources are not possible. Therefore, for this model formulation, x_1, x_2, s_1, and $s_2 \geq 0$.

The complete linear programming model can be written in what is referred to as *standard form* with slack variables as follows:

$$\text{maximize } Z = \$40x_1 + \$50x_2 + 0s_1 + 0s_2$$
$$\text{subject to}$$
$$x_1 + 2x_2 + s_1 = 40$$
$$4x_1 + 3x_2 + s_2 = 120$$
$$x_1, x_2, s_1, s_2 \geq 0$$

Figure 13 shows the graphical solution of our example, with slack variables included at each solution point.

Management Science Application

Estimating Food Nutrient Values at Minnesota's Nutrition Coordinating Center

The Nutrition Coordinating Center (NCC) at the University of Minnesota maintains a food composition database used by institutions around the world. This database is used to calculate dietary material intake; to plan menus; to explore the relationships between diet and disease; to meet regulatory requirements; and to monitor the effects of education, intervention, and regulation. These calculations require an enormous amount of nutrient value data for different food products.

Every year, over 12,000 new brand-name food products are introduced into the marketplace. However, it's not feasible to perform a chemical analysis on all foods for multiple nutrients, and so the NCC *estimates* thousands of nutrient values each year. The NCC has used a time-consuming trial-and-error approach to estimating these nutrient values. These estimates are a composite of the foods already in the database. The NCC developed a linear programming model that determines ingredient amounts in new food products. These estimated ingredient amounts are subsequently used to calculate nutrient amounts for a food product. The nutritionist normally uses the linear programming model to derive an initial estimate of ingredient amounts and then fine-tunes these amounts. The model has reduced the average time it takes to estimate a product formula from 8.3 minutes (using the trial-and-error approach) to 2.1 minutes labor time and effort.

Photo courtesy of Nutrition Coordinating Center

Source: B. J. Westrich, M. A. Altmann, and S. J. Potthoff, "Minnesota's Nutrition Coordinating Center Uses Mathematical Optimization to Estimate Food Nutrient Values," *Interfaces* 28, no. 5 (September–October 1998): 86–99.

Figure 13

Solutions at points *A*, *B*, and *C* with slack

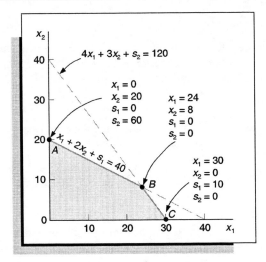

Summary of the Graphical Solution Steps

The steps for solving a graphical linear programming model are summarized here:

1. Plot the model constraints as equations on the graph; then, considering the inequalities of the constraints, indicate the feasible solution area.

2. Plot the objective function; then move this line out from the origin to locate the optimal solution point.
3. Solve simultaneous equations at the solution point to find the optimal solution values.

Or

2. Solve simultaneous equations at each corner point to find the solution values at each point.
3. Substitute these values into the objective function to find the set of values that results in the maximum Z value.

A Minimization Model Example

As we mentioned at the beginning of this chapter, there are two types of linear programming problems, a maximization problem (like the Beaver Creek Pottery Company example) and a minimization problem. A minimization problem is formulated the same basic way as a maximization problem, except for a few minor differences. The following example problem will demonstrate the formulation of a minimization model.

A farmer is preparing to plant a crop in the spring and needs to fertilize a field. There are two brands of fertilizer to choose from, Super-gro and Crop-quick. Each brand yields a specific amount of nitrogen and phosphate, as follows:

| | Chemical Contribution | |
| | NITROGEN | PHOSPHATE |
Brand	(LB/BAG)	(LB/BAG)
Super-gro	2	4
Crop-quick	4	3

The farmer's field requires at least 16 pounds of nitrogen and 24 pounds of phosphate. Super-gro costs $6 per bag, and Crop-quick costs $3. The farmer wants to know how many bags of each brand to purchase in order to minimize the total cost of fertilizing.

Decision Variables

This problem contains two decision variables representing the number of bags of each brand of fertilizer to purchase.

$$x_1 = \text{bags of Super-gro}$$
$$x_2 = \text{bags of Crop-quick}$$

The Objective Function

The farmer's objective is to minimize the total cost of fertilizing. The total cost is the sum of the individual costs of each type of fertilizer purchased. The objective function that represents total cost is expressed as

$$\text{minimize } Z = \$6x_1 + 3x_2$$

where

$$\$6x_1 = \text{cost of bags of Super-gro}$$
$$3x_2 = \text{cost of bags of Crop-quick}$$

Model Constraints

The requirements for nitrogen and phosphate represent the constraints of the model. Each bag of fertilizer contributes a number of pounds of nitrogen and phosphate to the field. The constraint for nitrogen is

$$2x_1 + 4x_2 \geq 16 \text{ lb}$$

where

$2x_1$ = the nitrogen contribution (lb) per bag of Super-gro
$4x_2$ = the nitrogen contribution (lb) per bag of Crop-quick

Rather than a ≤ (less than or equal to) inequality, as used in the Beaver Creek Pottery Company model, this constraint requires a ≥ (greater than or equal to) inequality. This is because the nitrogen content for the field is a minimum requirement specifying that at least 16 pounds of nitrogen be deposited on the farmer's field. If a minimum cost solution results in more than 16 pounds of nitrogen on the field, that is acceptable; however, the amount cannot be less than 16 pounds.

The constraint for phosphate is constructed like the constraint for nitrogen.

$$4x_1 + 3x_2 \geq 24 \text{ lb}$$

The three types of linear programming constraints are ≤, =, and ≥.

With this example we have shown two of the three types of linear programming model constraints, ≤ and ≥. The third type is an exact equality, =. This type specifies that a constraint requirement must be exact. For example, if the farmer had said the phosphate requirement for the field was exactly 24 pounds, the constraint would have been

$$4x_1 + 3x_2 = 24 \text{ lb}$$

As in our maximization model, there are also nonnegativity constraints in this problem to indicate that negative bags of fertilizer cannot be purchased.

$$x_1, x_2 \geq 0$$

The complete model formulation for this minimization problem is

minimize $Z = \$6x_1 + 3x_2$
subject to
$2x_1 + 4x_2 \geq 16$ lb of nitrogen
$4x_1 + 3x_2 \geq 24$ lb of phosphate
$x_1, x_2 \geq 0$

Graphical Solution of a Minimization Model

We follow the same basic steps in the graphical solution of a minimization model as we did in a maximization model. The fertilizer example will be used to demonstrate the graphical solution of a minimization model.

The first step is to graph the equations of the two model constraints, as shown in Figure 14. Next, the feasible solution area is chosen to reflect the ≥ inequalities in the constraints, as shown in Figure 15.

The optimal solution of a minimization problem is at the extreme point closest to the origin.

After the feasible solution area has been determined, the second step in the graphical solution approach is to locate the optimal point. Recall that in a maximization problem, the optimal solution is on the boundary of the feasible solution area that contains those points farthest from the origin. The optimal solution point in a minimization problem is also on the boundary of the feasible solution area; however, the boundary contains those points *closest* to the origin (zero being the lowest cost possible).

Figure 14

Constraint lines for fertilizer model

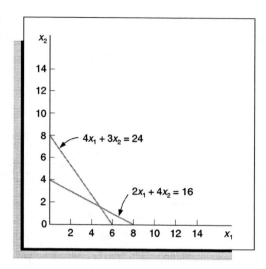

Figure 15

Feasible solution area

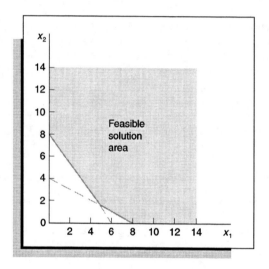

As in a maximization problem, the optimal solution is located at one of the extreme points of the boundary. In this case the corner points represent extremities in the boundary of the feasible solution area that are *closest* to the origin. Figure 16 shows the three corner points—*A*, *B*, and *C*—and the objective function line.

As the objective function edges *toward* the origin, the last point it touches in the feasible solution area is *A*. In other words, point *A* is the closest the objective function can get to the origin without encompassing infeasible points. Thus, it corresponds to the lowest cost that can be attained.

The final step in the graphical solution approach is to solve for the values of x_1 and x_2 at point *A*. Because point *A* is on the x_2 axis, $x_1 = 0$; thus,

$$4(0) + 3x_2 = 24$$
$$x_2 = 8$$

Figure 16

The optimal solution point

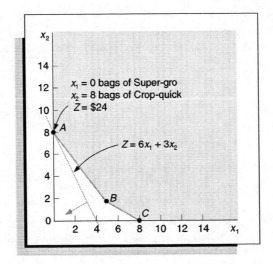

Given that the optimal solution is $x_1 = 0$, $x_2 = 8$, the minimum cost, Z, is

$$Z = \$6x_1 + 3x_2$$
$$Z = 6(0) + 3(8)$$
$$= \$24$$

This means the farmer should not purchase any Super-gro but, instead, should purchase eight bags of Crop-quick at a total cost of $24.

Management Science Application

Chemical Production at Monsanto

Monsanto produces maleic anhydride (a chemical used in making plastic) at plants in St. Louis and Pensacola. The combined capacity of the two plants is more than 45% of total U.S. output of 359 million pounds per year. Capacity at both plants exceeded demand, resulting in a need to assign production to each plant in an optimal manner. Three linear programming models were developed for this purpose, including a global model to determine the amount produced at each plant and individual plant models to adjust operating plans during a production period. The models, which encompassed over a thousand variables and a dozen or more constraints, minimize cost subject to meeting a production target. Use of the system has resulted in estimated annual savings of between $1 million and $3 million (depending on plant operating rules).

Photo courtesy of Exxon Chemical Company/Baytown Refinery

Source: R. Boykin, "Optimizing Chemical Production at Monsanto," *Interfaces* 15, no. 1 (January–February 1985): 88–95.

Surplus Variables

Greater than or equal to constraints cannot be converted to equations by adding slack variables as we did with ≤ constraints. Recall our fertilizer model formulated as

$$\text{minimize } Z = \$6x_1 + 3x_2$$
subject to

$$2x_1 + 4x_2 \geq 16 \text{ lb of nitrogen}$$
$$4x_1 + 3x_2 \geq 24 \text{ lb of phosphate}$$
$$x_1, x_2 \geq 0$$

where
x_1 = bags of Super-gro fertilizer
x_2 = bags of Crop-quick fertilizer
Z = farmer's total cost ($) of purchasing fertilizer

A surplus variable is subtracted from a ≥ constraint to convert it to an equation (=).

*A **surplus variable** represents an excess above a constraint requirement level.*

Because this problem has ≥ constraints as opposed to the ≤ constraints of the Beaver Creek Pottery Company maximization example, the constraints are converted to equations a little differently.

Instead of adding a slack variable with a ≥ constraint, we subtract a *surplus variable*. Whereas a slack variable is added and reflects unused resources, a surplus variable is subtracted and reflects the excess above a minimum resource requirement level. Like the slack variable, a surplus variable is represented symbolically by s_1 and must be nonnegative.

For the nitrogen constraint the subtraction of a surplus variable gives

$$2x_1 + 4x_2 - s_1 = 16$$

The surplus variable s_1 transforms the nitrogen constraint into an equation.

As an example, consider the hypothetical solution

$$x_1 = 0$$
$$x_2 = 10$$

Substituting these values into the previous equation yields

$$2(0) + 4(10) - s_1 = 16$$
$$-s_1 = 16 - 40$$
$$s_1 = 24 \text{ lb of nitrogen}$$

In this equation s_1 can be interpreted as the *extra* amount of nitrogen above the minimum requirement of 16 pounds that would be obtained by purchasing 10 bags of Crop-quick fertilizer.

In a similar manner, the constraint for phosphate is converted to an equation by subtracting a surplus variable, s_2,

$$4x_1 + 3x_2 - s_2 = 24$$

As was the case with slack variables, surplus variables contribute nothing to the overall cost of the model. For example, putting additional nitrogen or phosphate on the field will not affect the farmer's cost; the only thing affecting cost is the number of bags of fertilizer purchased. As such, the standard form of this linear programming model is summarized as

$$\text{minimize } Z = \$6x_1 + 3x_2 + 0s_1 + 0s_2$$
subject to
$$2x_1 + 4x_2 - s_1 = 16$$
$$4x_1 + 3x_2 - s_2 = 24$$
$$x_1, x_2, s_1, s_2 \geq 0$$

Figure 17 shows the graphical solutions for our example, with surplus variables included at each solution point.

Figure 17

Graph of the fertilizer example

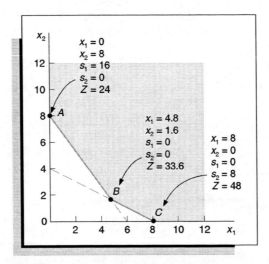

Irregular Types of Linear Programming Problems

For some linear programming models, the general rules do not always apply.

The basic forms of typical maximization and minimization problems have been shown in this chapter. However, there are several special types of atypical linear programming problems. Although these special cases do not occur frequently, they will be described so that you can recognize them when they arise. These special types include problems with more than one optimal solution, infeasible problems, and problems with unbounded solutions.

Multiple Optimal Solutions

Consider the Beaver Creek Pottery Company example with the objective function changed from $Z = 40x_1 + 50x_2$ to $Z = 40x_1 + 30x_2$.

$$\text{maximize } Z = 40x_1 + 30x_2$$
$$\text{subject to}$$
$$x_1 + 2x_2 \leq 40 \text{ hr of labor}$$
$$4x_1 + 3x_2 \leq 120 \text{ lb of clay}$$
$$x_1, x_2 \geq 0$$
$$\text{where}$$
$$x_1 = \text{bowls produced}$$
$$x_2 = \text{mugs produced}$$

The graph of this model is shown in Figure 18. The slight change in the objective function makes it now *parallel* to the constraint line, $4x_1 + 3x_2 = 120$. Both lines now have the same *slope* of $-4/3$. Therefore, as the objective function edge moves outward from the origin, it touches the whole line segment BC rather than a single extreme corner point before it leaves the feasible solution area. This means that every point along this line segment is optimal (i.e., each point results in the same profit of $Z = \$1,200$). The endpoints of this line segment, B and C, are typically referred to as the *alternate optimal solutions*. It is understood that these points represent the endpoints of a range of optimal solutions.

Alternate optimal solutions are at the endpoints of the constraint line segment that the objective function parallels.

23

Figure 18

Graph of the Beaver Creek Pottery Company example with multiple optimal solutions

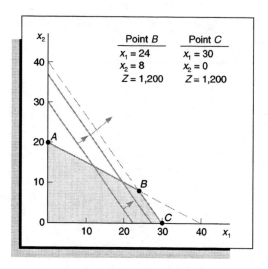

Multiple optimal solutions provide greater flexibility to the decision maker.

The pottery company, therefore, has several options in deciding on the number of bowls and mugs to produce. Multiple optimal solutions can benefit the decision maker because the number of decision options is enlarged. The multiple optimal solutions (along the line segment *BC* in Figure 18) allow the decision maker greater flexibility. For example, in the case of the Beaver Creek Pottery Company, it may be easier to sell bowls than mugs; thus, the solution at point *C* where only bowls are produced would be more desirable than the solution at point *B* where a mix of bowls and mugs is produced.

An Infeasible Problem

In some cases a linear programming problem has no feasible solution area; thus, there is no solution to the problem. An example of an infeasible problem is formulated next and depicted graphically in Figure 19.

Figure 19

Graph of an infeasible problem

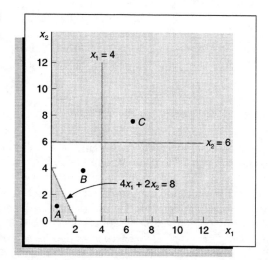

*An **infeasible problem** has no feasible solution area; every possible solution point violates one or more constraints.*

$$\text{maximize } Z = 5x_1 + 3x_2$$
$$\text{subject to}$$
$$4x_1 + 2x_2 \leq 8$$
$$x_1 \geq 4$$
$$x_2 \geq 6$$
$$x_1, x_2 \geq 0$$

Point A in Figure 19 satisfies only the constraint $4x_1 + 2x_2 \leq 8$, whereas point C satisfies only the constraints $x_1 \geq 4$ and $x_2 \geq 6$. Point B satisfies none of the constraints. The three constraints do not overlap to form a feasible solution area. Because no point satisfies all three constraints simultaneously, there is no solution to the problem. Infeasible problems do not typically occur, but when they do they are usually a result of errors in defining the problem or in formulating the linear programming model.

An Unbounded Problem

*In an **unbounded problem** the objective function can increase indefinitely without reaching a maximum value.*

In some problems the feasible solution area formed by the model constraints is not closed. In these cases it is possible for the objective function to increase indefinitely without ever reaching a maximum value, since it never reaches the boundary of the feasible solution area.

An example of this type of problem is formulated next and shown graphically in Figure 20.

$$\text{maximize } Z = 4x_1 + 2x_2$$
$$\text{subject to}$$
$$x_1 \geq 4$$
$$x_2 \leq 2$$
$$x_1, x_2 \geq 0$$

Figure 20

An unbounded problem

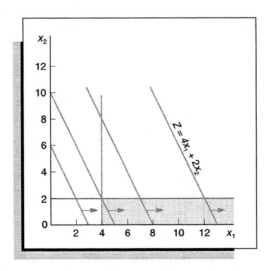

The solution space is not completely closed in.

In Figure 20 the objective function is shown to increase without bound; thus, a solution is never reached.

Unlimited profits are not possible in the real world; an unbounded solution, like an infeasible solution, typically reflects an error in defining the problem or in formulating the model.

Characteristics of Linear Programming Problems

The components of a linear programming model are an objective function, decision variables, and constraints.

Now that we have had the opportunity to construct several linear programming models, let's review the characteristics that identify a linear programming problem.

A linear programming problem requires a choice between alternative courses of action (i.e., a decision). The decision is represented in the model by decision variables. A typical choice task for a business firm is deciding how much of several different products to produce, as in the Beaver Creek Pottery Company example presented earlier in this chapter. Identifying the choice task and defining the decision variables is usually the first step in the formulation process because it is quite difficult to construct the objective function and constraints without first identifying the decision variables.

The problem encompasses an objective that the decision maker wants to achieve. The two most frequently encountered objectives for a business are maximizing profit and minimizing cost.

A third characteristic of a linear programming problem is that restrictions exist, making unlimited achievement of the objective function impossible. In a business firm these restrictions often take the form of limited resources such as labor or material; however, the example models in this chapter exhibited a variety of problem restrictions. These restrictions, as well as the objective, must be definable by mathematical functional relationships that are linear. Defining these relationships is typically the most difficult part of the formulation process.

Properties of Linear Programming Models

Proportionality means the slope of a constraint or objective function line is constant.

In addition to encompassing only linear relationships, a linear programming model also has several other implicit properties, which have been exhibited consistently throughout the examples in this chapter. The term *linear* not only means that the functions in the models are graphed as a straight line; it also means that the relationships exhibit *proportionality*. In other words, the rate of change, or slope, of the function is constant; therefore, changes of a given size in the value of a decision variable will result in exactly the same relative changes in the functional value.

The terms in the objective function or constraints are **additive**.

Linear programming also requires that the objective function terms and the constraint terms be *additive*. For example, in the Beaver Creek Pottery Company model, the total profit (Z) must equal the sum of profits earned from making bowls ($\$40x_1$) and mugs ($\$50x_2$). Also, the total resources used must equal the sum of the resources used for each activity in a constraint (e.g., labor).

The values of decision variables are continuous or **divisible**.

Another property of linear programming models is that the solution values (of the decision variables) cannot be restricted to integer values; the decision variables can take on any fractional value. Thus, the variables are said to be *continuous* or *divisible*, as opposed to *integer* or *discrete*. For example, although decision variables representing bowls or mugs or airplanes or automobiles should realistically have integer (whole number) solutions, the solution methods for linear programming will not necessarily provide such solutions. This is a property that will be discussed further as solution methods are presented in subsequent chapters.

All model parameters are assumed to be known with **certainty**.

The final property of linear programming models is that the values of all the model parameters are assumed to be constant and known with *certainty*. In real situations, however, model parameters are frequently uncertain, because they reflect the future as well as the present, and future conditions are rarely known with certainty.

To summarize, a linear programming model has the following general properties: linearity, proportionality, additivity, divisibility, and certainty. As various linear programming solution methods are presented throughout this book, these properties will become more obvious and their impact on problem solution will be discussed in greater detail.

Summary

The two example problems in this chapter were formulated as linear programming models in order to demonstrate the modeling process. These problems were similar in that they concerned achieving some objective subject to a set of restrictions or requirements. Linear programming models exhibit certain common characteristics:

- An objective function to be maximized or minimized
- A set of constraints
- Decision variables for measuring the level of activity
- Linearity among all constraint relationships and the objective function

The graphical approach to the solution of linear programming problems is not a very efficient means of solving problems. For one thing, drawing accurate graphs is tedious. Moreover, the graphical approach is limited to models with only two decision variables. However, the analysis of the graphical approach provides valuable insight into linear programming problems and their solutions.

In the graphical approach, once the feasible solution area and the optimal solution point have been determined from the graph, simultaneous equations are solved to determine the values of x_1 and x_2 at the solution point.

References

Baumol, W. J. *Economic Theory and Operations Analysis*. 4th ed. Englewood Cliffs, N.J.: Prentice-Hall, 1977.

Charnes, A., and Cooper, W. W. *Management Models and Industrial Applications of Linear Programming*. New York: John Wiley & Sons, 1961.

Dantzig, G. B. *Linear Programming and Extensions*. Princeton, N.J.: Princeton University Press, 1963.

Gass, S. *Linear Programming*. 4th ed. New York: McGraw-Hill, 1975.

Hadley, G. *Linear Programming*. Reading, Mass.: Addison-Wesley, 1962.

Hillier, F. S., and Lieberman, G. J. *Introduction to Operations Research*. 4th ed. San Francisco: Holden-Day, 1986.

Kwak, N. K. *Mathematical Programming with Business Applications*. New York: McGraw-Hill, 1973.

Llewellyn, R. W. *Linear Programming*. New York: Holt, Rinehart and Winston, 1964.

Taha, H. A. *Operations Research, an Introduction*. 4th ed. New York: Macmillan, 1987.

Wagner, H. M. *Principles of Operations Research*. 2nd ed. Englewood Cliffs, N.J.: Prentice-Hall, 1975.

Example Problem Solutions

As a prelude to the problems, this section presents example solutions to two linear programming problems.

Problem Statement

Moore's Meatpacking Company produces a hot dog mixture in 1,000-pound batches. The mixture contains two ingredients—chicken and beef. The cost per pound of each of these ingredients is as follows:

Ingredient	Cost/lb
Chicken	$3
Beef	$5

Each batch has the following recipe requirements:

a. At least 500 pounds of chicken
b. At least 200 pounds of beef

The ratio of chicken to beef must be at least 2 to 1. The company wants to know the optimal mixture of ingredients that will minimize cost. Formulate a linear programming model for this problem.

Solution

Step 1: Identify Decision Variables

Recall that the problem should not be "swallowed whole." Identify each part of the model separately, starting with the decision variables.

$$x_1 = \text{lb of chicken}$$
$$x_2 = \text{lb of beef}$$

Step 2: Formulate the Objective Function

$$\text{minimize } Z = \$3x_1 + \$5x_2$$
where
$$Z = \text{cost per 1,000-lb batch}$$
$$\$3x_1 = \text{cost of chicken}$$
$$\$5x_2 = \text{cost of beef}$$

Step 3: Establish Model Constraints

The constraints of this problem are embodied in the recipe restrictions and (not to be overlooked) the fact that each batch must consist of 1,000 pounds of mixture.

$$x_1 + x_2 = 1,000 \text{ lb}$$
$$x_1 \geq 500 \text{ lb of chicken}$$
$$x_2 \geq 200 \text{ lb of beef}$$
$$x_1/x_2 \geq 2/1 \text{ or } x_1 - 2x_2 \geq 0$$

and

$$x_1, x_2 \geq 0$$

The Model

$$\text{minimize } Z = \$3x_1 + \$5x_2$$
subject to
$$x_1 + x_2 = 1,000$$
$$x_1 \geq 500$$
$$x_2 \geq 200$$
$$x_1 - 2x_2 \geq 0$$
$$x_1, x_2 \geq 0$$

Problem Statement

Solve the following linear programming model graphically:

$$\text{maximize } Z = 4x_1 + 5x_2$$
subject to
$$x_1 + 2x_2 \leq 10$$
$$6x_1 + 6x_2 \leq 36$$
$$x_1 \leq 4$$
$$x_1, x_2 \geq 0$$

Solution

Step 1: Plot the Constraint Lines as Equations

A simple method for plotting constraint lines is to set one of the constraint variables equal to zero and solve for the other variable to establish a point on one of the axes. The three constraint lines are graphed in Figure 21.

Figure 21

The constraint equations

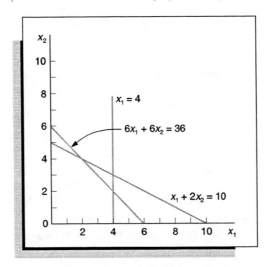

Step 2: Determine the Feasible Solution Area

The feasible solution area is determined by identifying the space that jointly satisfies the $\leq$ conditions of all three constraints. (See Figure 22.)

Figure 22

The feasible solution space and extreme points

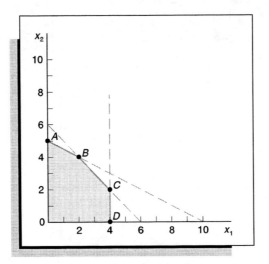

Step 3: Determine the Solution Points

The solution at point A can be determined by noting that the constraint line intersects the x_2 axis at 5; thus, $x_2 = 5$, $x_1 = 0$, and $Z = 25$. The solution at point D on the other axis can be determined similarly; the constraint intersects the axis at $x_1 = 4$, $x_2 = 0$, and $Z = 16$.

The values at points B and C must be found by solving simultaneous equations. Note that point B is formed by the intersection of the lines $x_1 + 2x_2 = 10$ and $6x_1 + 6x_2 = 36$. First convert both of these equations to functions of x_1.

$$x_1 + 2x_2 = 10$$
$$x_1 = 10 - 2x_2$$

and

$$6x_1 + 6x_2 = 36$$
$$6x_1 = 36 - 6x_2$$
$$x_1 = 6 - x_2$$

Now set the equations equal and solve for x_2.

$$10 - 2x_2 = 6 - x_2$$
$$-x_2 = -4$$
$$x_2 = 4$$

Substituting $x_2 = 4$ into either of the two equations gives a value for x_1:

$$x_1 = 6 - x_2$$
$$x_1 = 6 - (4)$$
$$x_1 = 2$$

Thus, at point B, $x_1 = 2$, $x_2 = 4$, and $Z = 28$.

At point C, $x_1 = 4$. Substituting $x_1 = 4$ into the equation $x_1 = 6 - x_2$ gives a value for x_2:

$$4 = 6 - x_2$$
$$x_2 = 2$$

Thus, $x_1 = 4$, $x_2 = 2$, and $Z = 26$.

Step 4: Determine the Optimal Solution

The optimal solution is at point B, where $x_1 = 2$, $x_2 = 4$, and $Z = 28$. The optimal solution and solutions at the other extreme points are summarized in Figure 23.

Figure 23

Optimal solution point

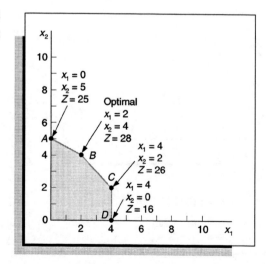

30

Problems

1. A company makes products 1 and 2 from two resources. The linear programming model for determining the amounts of product 1 and 2 to produce (i.e., x_1 and x_2) is

$$\text{maximize } Z = 8x_1 + 2x_2 \text{ (profit, \$)}$$
$$\text{subject to}$$
$$4x_1 + 5x_2 \leq 20 \text{ (resource 1, lb)}$$
$$2x_1 + 6x_2 \leq 18 \text{ (resource 2, lb)}$$
$$x_1, x_2 \geq 0$$

Solve this model graphically.

2. A company produces two products that are processed on two assembly lines. Assembly line 1 has 100 available hours, and assembly line 2 has 42 available hours. Each product requires 10 hours of processing time on line 1, while on line 2 product 1 requires 7 hours and product 2 requires 3 hours. The profit for product 1 is $6 per unit, and the profit for product 2 is $4 per unit.
   a. Formulate a linear programming model for this problem.
   b. Solve this model using graphical analysis.

3. The Munchies Cereal Company makes a cereal from several ingredients. Two of the ingredients, oats and rice, provide vitamins A and B. The company wants to know how many ounces of oats and rice it should include in each box of cereal to meet the minimum requirements of 48 milligrams of vitamin A and 12 milligrams of vitamin B while minimizing cost. An ounce of oats contributes 8 milligrams of vitamin A and 1 milligram of vitamin B, whereas an ounce of rice contributes 6 milligrams of A and 2 milligrams of B. An ounce of oats costs $0.05, and an ounce of rice costs $0.03.
   a. Formulate a linear programming model for this problem.
   b. Solve this model using graphical analysis.

4. What would be the effect on the optimal solution in problem 3 if the cost of rice increased from $0.03 per ounce to $0.06 per ounce?

5. The Kalo Fertilizer Company makes a fertilizer using two chemicals that provide nitrogen, phosphate, and potassium. A pound of ingredient 1 contributes 10 ounces of nitrogen and 6 ounces of phosphate, while a pound of ingredient 2 contributes 2 ounces of nitrogen, 6 ounces of phosphate, and 1 ounce of potassium. Ingredient 1 costs $3 per pound, and ingredient 2 costs $5 per pound. The company wants to know how many pounds of each chemical ingredient to put into a bag of fertilizer to meet minimum requirements of 20 ounces of nitrogen, 36 ounces of phosphate, and 2 ounces of potassium while minimizing cost.
   a. Formulate a linear programming model for this problem.
   b. Solve this model using graphical analysis.

6. The Pinewood Furniture Company produces chairs and tables from two resources—labor and wood. The company has 80 hours of labor and 36 pounds of wood available each day. Demand for chairs is limited to 6 per day. Each chair requires 8 hours of labor and 2 pounds of wood to produce, whereas a table requires 10 hours of labor and 6 pounds of wood. The profit derived from each chair is $400 and from each table, $100. The company wants to determine the number of chairs and tables to produce each day in order to maximize profit.
   a. Formulate a linear programming model for this problem.
   b. Solve this model using graphical analysis.

7. In problem 6, how much labor and wood will be unused if the optimal numbers of chairs and tables are produced?

8. In problem 6, explain the effect on the optimal solution of changing the profit on a table from $100 to $500.

9. The Crumb and Custard Bakery makes coffee cakes and Danish in large pans. The main ingredients are flour and sugar. There are 25 pounds of flour and 16 pounds of sugar available and the demand for coffee cakes is 5. Five pounds of flour and 2 pounds of sugar are required to make a pan of coffee cake, and 5 pounds of flour and 4 pounds of sugar are required to make a pan of Danish. A pan of coffee cakes has a profit of $1, and a pan of Danish has a profit of $5. Determine the number of pans of cakes and Danish to produce each day so that profit will be maximized.
    a. Formulate a linear programming model for this problem.
    b. Solve this model using graphical analysis.

10. In problem 9, how much flour and sugar will be left unused if the optimal numbers of cakes and Danish are baked?

11. Solve the following linear programming model graphically:

$$\text{maximize } Z = 3x_1 + 6x_2$$
$$\text{subject to}$$
$$3x_1 + 2x_2 \leq 18$$
$$x_1 + x_2 \geq 5$$
$$x_1 \leq 4$$
$$x_1, x_2 \geq 0$$

12. The Elixer Drug Company produces a drug from two ingredients. Each ingredient contains the same three antibiotics in different proportions. One gram of ingredient 1 contributes 3 units, and ingredient 2 contributes 1 unit of antibiotic 1; the drug requires 6 units. At least 4 units of antibiotic 2 are required, and the ingredients each contribute 1 unit per gram. At least 12 units of antibiotic 3 are required; a gram of ingredient 1 contributes 2 units, and a gram of ingredient 2 contributes 6 units. The cost for a gram of ingredient 1 is $80, and the cost for a gram of ingredient 2 is $50. The company wants to formulate a linear programming model to determine the number of grams of each ingredient that must go into the drug in order to meet the antibiotic requirements at the minimum cost.
    a. Formulate a linear programming model for this problem.
    b. Solve this model using graphical analysis.

13. A jewelry store makes necklaces and bracelets from gold and platinum. The store has 18 ounces of gold and 20 ounces of platinum. Each necklace requires 3 ounces of gold and 2 ounces of platinum, whereas each bracelet requires 2 ounces of gold and 4 ounces of platinum. The demand for bracelets is no more than 4. A necklace earns $300 in profit and a bracelet, $400. The store wants to determine the number of necklaces and bracelets to make in order to maximize profit.
    a. Formulate a linear programming model for this problem.
    b. Solve this model using graphical analysis.

14. In problem 13, explain the effect on the optimal solution of increasing the profit on a bracelet from $400 to $600. What will be the effect of changing the platinum requirement for a necklace from 2 ounces to 3 ounces?

15. In problem 13:
    a. The maximum demand for bracelets is four. If the store produces the optimal number of bracelets and necklaces, will the maximum demand for bracelets be met? If not, by how much will it be missed?
    b. What profit for a necklace would result in no bracelets being produced, and what would be the optimal solution for this profit?

16. A clothier makes coats and slacks. The two resources required are wool cloth and labor. The clothier has 150 square yards of wool and 200 hours of labor available. Each coat requires 3 square yards of wool and 10 hours of labor, whereas each pair of slacks requires 5 square yards of wool and 4 hours of labor. The profit for a coat is $50, and the profit for slacks is $40. The clothier wants to determine the number of coats and pairs of slacks to make so that profit will be maximized.
    a. Formulate a linear programming model for this problem.
    b. Solve this model using graphical analysis.

17. In problem 16, what would be the effect on the optimal solution if the available labor were increased from 200 to 240 hours?

18. Solve the following linear programming model graphically:

$$\text{maximize } Z = 1.5x_1 + x_2$$

subject to

$$x_1 \le 4$$
$$x_2 \le 6$$
$$x_1 + x_2 \le 5$$
$$x_1, x_2 \ge 0$$

19. Transform the model in problem 18 into standard form and indicate the value of the slack variables at each corner point solution.

20. Solve the following linear programming model graphically:

$$\text{maximize } Z = 5x_1 + 8x_2$$

subject to

$$3x_1 + 5x_2 \le 50$$
$$2x_1 + 4x_2 \le 40$$
$$x_1 \le 8$$
$$x_2 \le 10$$
$$x_1, x_2 \ge 0$$

21. Transform the model in problem 20 into standard form and indicate the value of the slack variables at each corner point solution.

22. Solve the following linear programming model graphically:

$$\text{maximize } Z = 6.5x_1 + 10x_2$$

subject to

$$2x_1 + 4x_2 \le 40$$
$$x_1 + x_2 \le 15$$
$$x_1 \ge 8$$
$$x_1, x_2 \ge 0$$

23. In problem 22, if the constraint $x_1 \geq 8$ is changed to $x_1 \leq 8$, what effect does this have on the feasible solution space and the optimal solution?

24. Universal Claims Processors processes insurance claims for large national insurance companies. Most claim processing is done by a large pool of computer operators, some of whom are permanent and some temporary. A permanent operator can process 16 claims per day, whereas a temporary operator can process 12 per day, and on average the company processes at least 450 claims each day. The company has 40 computer workstations. A permanent operator will generate about 0.5 claims with errors each day, whereas a temporary operator averages about 1.4 defective claims per day. The company wants to limit claims with errors to 25 per day. A permanent operator is paid \$64 per day and a temporary operator is paid \$42 per day. The company wants to determine the number of permanent and temporary operators to hire in order to minimize costs.
    a. Formulate a linear programming model for this problem.
    b. Solve this model using graphical analysis.

25. In problem 24, explain the effect on the optimal solution of changing the daily pay for a permanent claims processor from \$64 to \$54. Explain the effect of changing the daily pay for a temporary claims processor from \$42 to \$36.

26. In problem 24, what would be the effect on the optimal solution if Universal Claims Processors decided not to try to limit the number of defective claims each day?

27. In problem 24, explain the effect on the optimal solution if the minimum number of claims the firm processes each day increases from 450 to at least 650.

28. Solve the following linear programming model graphically:

$$\text{minimize } Z = 8x_1 + 6x_2$$

subject to

$$4x_1 + 2x_2 \geq 20$$
$$-6x_1 + 4x_2 \leq 12$$
$$x_1 + x_2 \geq 6$$
$$x_1, x_2 \geq 0$$

29. Solve the following linear programming model graphically:

$$\text{minimize } Z = 3x_1 + 6x_2$$

subject to

$$3x_1 + 2x_2 \leq 18$$
$$x_1 + x_2 \geq 5$$
$$x_1 \leq 4$$
$$x_2 \leq 7$$
$$x_2/x_1 \leq 7/8$$
$$x_1, x_2 \geq 0$$

30. In problem 29, what would be the effect on the solution if the constraint $x_2 \leq 7$ is changed to $x_2 \geq 7$?

31. Solve the following linear programming model graphically:

$$\text{minimize } Z = 5x_1 + x_2$$

subject to

$$3x_1 + 4x_2 = 24$$
$$x_1 \leq 6$$
$$x_1 + 3x_2 \leq 12$$
$$x_1, x_2 \geq 0$$

32. Solve the following linear programming model graphically:

$$\text{maximize } Z = 3x_1 + 2x_2$$

subject to

$$2x_1 + 4x_2 \leq 22$$
$$-x_1 + 4x_2 \leq 10$$
$$4x_1 - 2x_2 \leq 14$$
$$x_1 - 3x_2 \leq 1$$
$$x_1, x_2 \geq 0$$

33. Solve the following linear programming model graphically:

$$\text{minimize } Z = 8x_1 + 2x_2$$

subject to

$$2x_1 - 6x_2 \leq 12$$
$$5x_1 + 4x_2 \geq 40$$
$$x_1 + 2x_2 \geq 12$$
$$x_2 \leq 6$$
$$x_1, x_2 \geq 0$$

34. Gillian's Restaurant has an ice-cream counter where it sells two main products, ice cream and frozen yogurt, each in a variety of flavors. The restaurant makes one order for ice cream and yogurt each week, and the store has enough freezer space for 115 gallons of both products. A gallon of frozen yogurt costs $0.75 and a gallon of ice cream costs $0.93, and the restaurant budgets $90 each week for these products. The manager estimates that each week the restaurant sells at least twice as much ice cream as frozen yogurt. Profit per gallon of ice cream is $4.15 and profit per gallon of yogurt is $3.60.
    a. Formulate a linear programming model for this problem.
    b. Solve this model using graphical analysis.

35. In problem 34, how much additional profit would the restaurant realize each week if it increased its freezer capacity to accommodate 20 extra gallons of ice cream and yogurt?

36. The Copperfield Mining Company owns two mines, each of which produces three grades of ore—high, medium, and low. The company has a contract to supply a smelting company with at least 12 tons of high-grade ore, 8 tons of medium-grade ore, and 24 tons of low-grade ore. Each mine produces a certain amount of each type of ore during each hour that it operates. Mine 1 produces 6 tons of high-grade ore, 2 tons of medium-grade ore, and 4 tons of low-grade ore per hour. Mine 2 produces 2, 2, and 12 tons, respectively, of high-, medium-, and low-grade ore per hour. It costs Copperfield $200 per hour to mine each ton of ore from mine 1, and $160 per hour to mine a ton of ore from mine 2. The company wants to determine the number of hours it needs to operate each mine so that its contractual obligations can be met at the lowest cost.
    a. Formulate a linear programming model for this problem.
    b. Solve this model using graphical analysis.

37. A canning company produces two sizes of cans—regular and large. The cans are produced in 10,000-can lots. The cans are processed through a stamping operation and a coating operation. The company has 30 days available for both stamping and coating. A lot of regular-size cans requires 2 days to stamp and 4 days to coat, whereas a lot of large cans requires 4 days to stamp and 2 days to coat. A lot of regular-size cans earns $800 profit, and a lot of large-size cans earns $900 profit. In

order to fulfill its obligations under a shipping contract, the company must produce at least 9 lots. The company wants to determine the number of lots to produce of each size can (x_1 and x_2) in order to maximize profit.
   a. Formulate a linear programming model for this problem.
   b. Solve this model using graphical analysis.

38. A manufacturing firm produces two products. Each product must undergo an assembly process and a finishing process. It is then transferred to the warehouse, which has space for only a limited number of items. The firm has 80 hours available for assembly and 112 hours for finishing, and it can store a maximum of 10 units in the warehouse. Each unit of product 1 has a profit of $30 and requires 4 hours to assemble and 14 hours to finish. Each unit of product 2 has a profit of $70 and requires 10 hours to assemble and 8 hours to finish. The firm wants to determine the quantity of each product to produce in order to maximize profit.
   a. Formulate a linear programming model for this problem.
   b. Solve this model using graphical analysis.

39. Assume that the objective function in problem 38 has been changed from $Z = 30x_1 + 70x_2$ to $Z = 90x_1 + 70x_2$. Determine the slope of each objective function and discuss what effect these slopes have on the optimal solution.

40. The Valley Wine Company produces two kinds of wine—Valley Nectar and Valley Red. The wines are produced from 64 tons of grapes the company has acquired this season. A 1,000-gallon batch of Nectar requires 4 tons of grapes and a batch of Red requires 8 tons. However, production is limited by the availability of only 50 cubic yards of storage space for aging and 120 hours of processing time. A batch of each type of wine requires 5 yd^3 of storage space. The processing time for a batch of Nectar is 15 hours and the processing time for a batch of Red is 8 hours. Demand for each type of wine is limited to 7 batches. The profit for a batch of Nectar is $9,000 and the profit for a batch of Red is $12,000. The company wants to determine the number of 1,000-gallon batches of Nectar (x_1) and Red (x_2) to produce in order to maximize profit.
   a. Formulate a linear programming model for this problem.
   b. Solve this model using graphical analysis.

41. In problem 40:
   a. How much processing time will be left unused at the optimal solution?
   b. What would be the effect on the optimal solution of increasing the available storage space from 50 to 60 yd^3?

42. Kroeger supermarket sells its own brand of canned peas as well as several national brands. The store makes a profit of $0.28 per can for its own peas and a profit of $0.19 for any of the national brands. The store has 6 square feet of shelf space available for canned peas and each can of peas takes up 9 square inches of that space. Electronic sales records show that each week the store never sells more than one-half as many cans of its own brand as it does of the national brands. The store wants to know how many cans of its own brand of peas and how many cans of the national brands to stock each week on the allocated shelf space in order to maximize profit.
   a. Formulate a linear programming model for this problem.
   b. Solve this model using graphical analysis.

43. In problem 42, if Kroeger discounts the price of its own brand of peas, the store will sell at least 1.5 times as much of the national brands as its own brand, but its profit margin on its own brand will be reduced to $0.23 per can. What effect would the discount have on the optimal solution?

44. Shirtstop makes T-shirts with logos and sells them in its chain of retail stores. It contracts with two different plants—one in Puerto Rico and one in the Bahamas. The shirts from the plant in Puerto Rice cost $0.46 apiece and 9% of them are defective and can't be sold. The shirts from the Bahamas cost only $0.35 each but they have an 18% defective rate. Shirtstop needs 3,500 shirts. To retain its relationship with the two plants it wants to order at least 1,000 shirts from each. It would also like at least 88% of the shirts it receives to be saleable.
    a. Formulate a linear programming model for this problem.
    b. Solve this model using graphical analysis.

45. In problem 44:
    a. Suppose Shirtstop decided it wanted to minimize the defective shirts while keeping costs below $2,000. Reformulate the problem with these changes and solve graphically.
    b. How many fewer defective items were achieved with the model in (a) than the model in problem 44?

46. Angela and Bob Ray keep a large garden in which they grow cabbage, tomatoes, and onions to make two kinds of relish—chow-chow and tomato. The chow-chow is made primarily of cabbage, whereas the tomato relish is made mostly from tomatoes. Both relishes include onions, bell peppers, and spices. A jar of chow-chow contains 8 ounces of cabbage, 3 ounces of tomatoes, and 3 ounces of onions, whereas a jar of tomato relish contains 6 ounces of tomatoes, 6 ounces of cabbage, and 2 ounces of onions. The Rays grow 120 pounds of cabbage, 90 pounds of tomatoes, and 45 pounds of onions each summer. The Rays can produce no more than 24 dozen jars of relish. They make $2.25 in profit from a jar of chow-chow and $1.95 in profit from a jar of tomato relish. The Rays want to know how many jars of each kind of relish to produce to generate the most profit.
    a. Formulate a linear programming model for this problem.
    b. Solve this model graphically.

47. In problem 46, the Rays have checked their sales records for the past five years and have found that they sell at least 50% more chow-chow than tomato relish. How will this additional information affect their model and solution?

48. A California grower has a 50-acre farm on which to plant strawberries and tomatoes. The grower has available 300 hours of labor per week and 800 tons of fertilizer, and has contracted for shipping space for a maximum of 26 acres' worth of strawberries and 37 acres' worth of tomatoes. An acre of strawberries requires 10 hours of labor and 8 tons of fertilizer, whereas an acre of tomatoes requires 3 hours of labor and 20 tons of fertilizer. The profit from an acre of strawberries is $400, and the profit from an acre of tomatoes is $300. The farmer wants to know the number of acres of strawberries and tomatoes to plant to maximize profit.
    a. Formulate a linear programming model for this problem.
    b. Solve this model using graphical analysis.

49. In problem 48, if the amount of fertilizer that was required for each acre of strawberries was determined to be 20 tons instead of 8 tons, what would be the effect on the optimal solution?

50. The admissions office at Tech wants to determine how many in-state and out-of-state students to accept for next fall's entering freshman class. Tuition for an in-state student is $7,600 per year

whereas out-of-state tuition is $22,500 per year. A total of 12,800 in-state and 8,100 out-of-state freshmen have applied for next fall and Tech does not want to accept more than 3,500 students. However, because Tech is a state institution, the state mandates that it can accept no more than 40% out-of-state students. From past experience the admissions office knows that 12% of in-state students and 24% of out-of-state students will drop out during their first year. Tech wants to maximize total tuition while limiting the total attrition to 600 first-year students.

    a. Formulate a linear programming model for this problem.

    b. Solve this model using graphical analysis.

51. Janet Lopez is establishing an investment portfolio that will include stock and bond funds. She has $720,000 to invest and she does not want the portfolio to include more than 65% stocks. The average annual return for the stock fund she plans to invest in is 18% whereas the average annual return for the bond fund is 6%. She further estimates that the most she could lose in the next year in the stock fund is 22% whereas the most she could lose in the bond fund is 5%. To reduce her risk she wants to limit her potential maximum losses to $100,000.

    a. Formulate a linear programming model for this problem.

    b. Solve this model using graphical analysis.

52. Solve the following linear programming model graphically and explain the solution result:

$$\text{minimize } Z = \$3{,}000x_1 + 1{,}000x_2$$
$$\text{subject to}$$
$$60x_1 + 20x_2 \geq 1{,}200$$
$$10x_1 + 10x_2 \geq 400$$
$$40x_1 + 160x_2 \geq 2{,}400$$
$$x_1, x_2 \geq 0$$

53. Solve the following linear programming model graphically and explain the solution result:

$$\text{maximize } Z = 60x_1 + 90x_2$$
$$\text{subject to}$$
$$60x_1 + 30x_2 \leq 1{,}500$$
$$100x_1 + 100x_2 \geq 6{,}000$$
$$x_2 \geq 30$$
$$x_1, x_2 \geq 0$$

54. Solve the following linear programming model graphically and explain the solution result:

$$\text{maximize } Z = 110x_1 + 75x_2$$
$$\text{subject to}$$
$$2x_1 + x_2 \geq 40$$
$$-6x_1 + 8x_2 \leq 120$$
$$70x_1 + 105x_2 \geq 2{,}100$$
$$x_1, x_2 \geq 0$$

METROPOLITAN POLICE PATROL

The Metropolitan Police Department had recently been criticized in the local media for not responding to police calls in the downtown area rapidly enough. In several recent cases, alarms had sounded for break-ins, but by the time the police car arrived, the perpetrators had left and in one instance a store owner had been shot. Sergeant Joe Davis had been assigned by the chief as head of a task force to find a way to determine optimal patrol area (dimensions) for their cars that would minimize the average time it took to respond to a call in the downtown area.

Sergeant Davis solicited help from Angela Maris, an analyst in the operations area for the police department. Together they began to work through the problem.

Joe noted to Angela that normal patrol sectors are laid out in rectangles, with each rectangle including a number of city blocks. For illustrative purposes he defined the dimensions of the sector as x in the horizontal direction and as y in the vertical direction. He explained to Angela that cars traveled in straight lines either horizontally or vertically and turned at right angles. Travel in a horizontal direction must be accompanied by travel in a vertical direction, and the total distance traveled is the sum of the horizontal and vertical segments. He further noted that past research on police patrolling in urban areas had shown that the average distance traveled by a patrol car responding to a call in either direction was one-third of the dimensions of the sector, or $x/3$ and $y/3$.

He also explained that the travel time it took to respond to a call (assuming a car left immediately upon receiving the call) is simply the average distance traveled divided by the average travel speed.

Angela told Joe that now that she understood how average travel time to a call was determined, she could see that it was closely related to the size of the patrol area. She asked Joe if there were any restrictions on the size of the area sectors that cars patrolled. He responded that for their city, the department believed that the perimeter of a patrol sector should not be less than 5 miles or exceed 12 miles. He noted several policy issues and manpower constraints that required these specifications. Angela wanted to know if any additional restrictions existed, and Joe indicated that the distance in the vertical direction must be at least 50% more than the horizontal distance for the sector. He explained that laying out sectors in that manner meant that the patrol areas would have a greater tendency to overlap different residential, income, and retail areas than if they ran the other way. He said that these areas were layered from north to south in the city. So if a sector area were laid out east to west, all of it would tend to be in one demographic layer.

Angela indicated that she had almost enough information to develop a model, except that she also needed to know the average travel speed the patrol cars could travel. Joe told her that cars moving vertically traveled an average of 15 miles per hour, whereas cars traveled horizontally an average of 20 miles per hour. He said that the difference was due to different traffic flows.

Develop a linear programming model for this problem, and solve it using the graphical method.

"THE POSSIBILITY" RESTAURANT

Angela Fox and Zooey Caulfield were food and nutrition majors at State University, as well as close friends and roommates. Upon graduation Angela and Zooey decided to open a French restaurant in Draperton, the small town where the university was located. There were no other French restaurants in Draperton, and the possibility of doing something new and somewhat risky intrigued the two friends. They purchased an old Victorian home just off Main Street for their new restaurant, which they named "The Possibility."

Angela and Zooey knew in advance that at least initially they could not offer a full, varied menu of dishes. They had no idea what their local customers' tastes in French cuisine would be, so they decided to serve only two full-course meals each night, one

with beef and the other with fish. Their chef, Pierre, was confident he could make each dish so exciting and unique that two meals would be sufficient, at least until they could assess which menu items were most popular. Pierre indicated that with each meal he could experiment with different appetizers, soups, salads, vegetable dishes, and desserts until they were able to identify a full selection of menu items.

The next problem for Angela and Zooey was to determine how many meals to prepare for each night so they could shop for ingredients and set up the work schedule. They could not afford too much waste. They estimated that they would sell a maximum of 60 meals each night. Each fish dinner, including all accompaniments, requires 15 minutes to prepare, and each beef dinner takes twice as long. There is a total of 20 hours of kitchen staff labor available each day. Angela and Zooey believe that because of the health consciousness of their potential clientele they will sell at least three fish dinners for every two beef dinners. However, they also believe that at least 10% of their customers will order beef dinners. The profit from each fish dinner will be approximately $12, and the profit from a beef dinner will be about $16.

Formulate a linear programming model for Angela and Zooey that will help them estimate the number of meals they should prepare each night and solve this model graphically.

If Angela and Zooey increased the menu price on the fish dinner so that the profit for both dinners was the same, what effect would that have on their solution? Suppose Angela and Zooey reconsidered the demand for beef dinners and decided that at least 20% of their customers would purchase beef dinners. What effect would this have on their meal preparation plan?

ANNABELLE INVESTS IN THE MARKET

Annabelle Sizemore has cashed in some treasury bonds and a life insurance policy that her parents had accumulated over the years for her. She has also saved some money in certificates of deposit and savings bonds during the 10 years since she graduated from college. As a result, she has $120,000 available to invest. Given the recent rise in the stock market she feels that she should invest all of this amount there. She has researched the market and has decided that she wants to invest in an index fund tied to S&P stocks and in an Internet stock fund. However, she is very concerned about the volatility of Internet stocks. Therefore, she wants to balance her risk to some degree.

She has decided to select an index fund from Shield Securities, and an Internet stock fund from the Madison Funds, Inc. She has also decided that the proportion of the dollar amount she invests in the index fund relative to the Internet fund should be at least one-third, but that she should not invest more than twice the amount in the Internet fund that she invests in the index fund. The price per share of the index fund is $175, whereas the price per share for the Internet fund is $208. The average annual return during the last 3 years for the index fund has been 17% and for the Internet stock fund it has been 28%. She anticipates that both mutual funds will realize the same average returns for the coming year that they have in the recent past; however, at the end of the year she is likely to reevaluate her investment strategy anyway. Thus, she wants to develop an investment strategy that will maximize her return for the coming year.

Formulate a linear programming model for Annabelle that will indicate how much money she should invest in each fund and solve this model using the graphical method.

Suppose Annabelle decides to change her risk balancing formula by eliminating the restriction that the proportion of the amount she invests in the index fund to the amount that she invests in the Internet fund must be at least one-third. What will the effect be on her solution? Suppose instead that she eliminates the restriction that the proportion of money she invests in the Internet fund relative to the stock fund not exceed a ratio of 2 to 1. How will this affect her solution?

If Annabelle can get one more dollar to invest, how will that affect her solution? Two more dollars? Three more dollars? What can you say about her return on her investment strategy given these successive changes?

Solutions to Selected Odd-Numbered Problems

1. $x_1 = 5, x_2 = 0, Z = 40$

3. (a) min. $Z = .05x_1 + .03x_2$; s.t. $8x_1 + 6x_2 \geq 48, x_1 + 2x_2 \geq 12, x_i \geq 0$; (b) $x_1 = 0, x_2 = 8, Z = 0.24$

5. (a) min. $Z = 3x_1 + 5x_2$; s.t. $10x_1 + 2x_2 \geq 20, 6x_1 + 6x_2 \geq 36, x_2 \geq 2$, $x_i \geq 0$; (b) $x_1 = 4, x_2 = 2, Z = 22$

7. No labor, 4.8 lb wood

9. (a) max. $Z = x_1 + 5x_2$; s.t. $5x_1 + 5x_2 \leq 25, 2x_1 + 4x_2 \leq 16, x_1 \leq 5, x_1, x_2 \geq 0$; (b) $x_1 = 0, x_2 = 4, Z = 20$

11. $x_1 = 0, x_2 = 9, Z = 54$

13. (a) max. $Z = 300x_1 + 400x_2$; s.t. $3x_1 + 2x_2 \leq 18, 2x_1 + 4x_2 \leq 20, x_2 \leq 4$, $x_1, x_2 \geq 0$; (b) $x_1 = 4, x_2 = 3, Z = 2,400$

15. (a) maximum demand is not achieved by one bracelet; (b) $600

17. $x_1 = 15.8, x_2 = 20.5, Z = 1,610$

19. A: $s_1 = 4, s_2 = 1, s_3 = 0$; B: $s_1 = 0, s_2 = 5, s_3 = 0$; C: $s_1 = 0, s_2 = 6, s_3 = 1$

21. A: $s_1 = 0, s_2 = 0, s_3 = 8, s_4 = 0$; B: $s_1 = 0, s_2 = 3.2, s_3 = 0, s_4 = 4.8$; C: $s_1 = 26, s_2 = 24, s_3 = 0, s_4 = 2$

23. changes the optimal solution

25. $x_1 = 28.125, x_2 = 0, Z = \$1,518.75$; no effect

27. infeasible solution

29. $x_1 = 4, x_2 = 1, Z = 18$

31. $x_1 = 4.8, x_2 = 2.4, Z = 26.4$

33. $x_1 = 3.2, x_2 = 6, Z = 37.6$

35. no additional profit

37. (a) max. $Z = 800x_1 + 900x_2$; s.t. $2x_1 + 4x_2 \leq 30, 4x_1 + 2x_2 \leq 30$, $x_1 + x_2 \geq 9, x_i \geq 0$; (b) $x_1 = 5, x_2 = 5, Z = 8,500$

39. $x_1 = 5.3, x_2 = 4.7, Z = 806$

41. (a) 12 hr; (b) new solution $- x_1 = 5.09, x_2 = 5.45, Z = 111.27$

43. $x_1 = 38.4, x_2 = 57.6, Z = 19.78$; profit reduced

45. (a) min. $Z = .09x_1 + .18x_2$, s.t. $.46x_1 + .35x_2 \leq 2,000, x_1 \geq 1,000$, $x_2 \geq 1,000, .91x_1 - .82x_2 \geq 3,500, x_1 \geq 0, x_2 \geq 0$; (b) 132 fewer defects

47. $x_1 = 160, x_2 = 106.67, Z = 568$

49. $x_1 = 25.71, x_2 = 14.29, Z = 14,571$

51. (a) max. $Z = .18x_1 + .06x_2$, s.t. $x_1 + x_2 \leq 720,000, x_1/(x_1 + x_2) \leq .65$, $.22x_1 + .05x_2 \leq 100,000, x_1, x_2 \geq 0$ (b) $x_1 = 376,470.59, x_2 = 343,526.41$, $Z = 83,376.47$

53. infeasible

Linear Programming: Computer Solution and Sensitivity Analysis

Computer Solution

Excel Spreadsheets • **QM for Windows**

Sensitivity Analysis

Changes in Objective Function Coefficients • **Objective Function Coefficient Ranges with the Computer** • **Changes in Constraint Quantity Values** • **Constraint Quantity Value Ranges with the Computer** • **Other Forms of Sensitivity Analysis** • **Shadow Prices**

Management Science Application: Grape Juice Management at Welch's

Summary • References • Example Problem Solution • Problems • Case Problems

The chapter on linear programming demonstrated how a linear programming model is formulated and how a solution can be derived from a graph of the model. Graphing can provide valuable insight into linear programming and linear programming solutions in general. However, the fact that this solution method is limited to problems with only two decision variables restricts its usefulness as a *general* solution technique.

In this chapter we will show how linear programming problems can be solved using several personal computer software packages. We will also describe how to use the computer solution result to experiment with a linear programming model to see what effect parameter changes will have on the optimal solution, referred to as *sensitivity analysis*.

Computer Solution

When linear programming was first developed in the 1940s, virtually the only way to solve a problem was using a lengthy manual mathematical solution procedure called the *simplex method*. However, during the next five decades as computer technology evolved, the computer was used more and more to solve linear programming models. The mathematical steps of the simplex method were simply programmed in prewritten software packages designed for the solution of linear programming problems. The ability to solve linear programming problems quickly and cheaply on the computer regardless of the size of the problem popularized linear programming and expanded its use by businesses. There currently are dozens of software packages with linear programming capabilities. Many of these are general-purpose management science or quantitative methods packages with linear programming modules among many other modules for other techniques. There are also numerous software packages that are devoted exclusively to linear programming and its derivatives. These packages are generally cheap, efficient, and easy to use.

As a result of the easy and low-cost availability of personal computers and linear programming software, the simplex method has become less of a focus in the teaching of linear programming. Thus, at this point in our presentation of linear programming we focus exclusively on computer solution. However, knowledge of the simplex method is useful in gaining an overall, in-depth understanding of linear programming for those who are interested in this degree of understanding. As was noted, computer solution itself is based on the simplex method. Thus, while we present linear programming in the text in a manner that does not require use of the simplex method, we also provide in-depth coverage of this topic on the CD that accompanies this text.

In the next few sections we demonstrate how to solve linear programming problems using Excel spreadsheets and QM for Windows, a typical general-purpose quantitative methods software package.

Excel Spreadsheets

Excel can be used to solve linear programming problems, although the data input requirements can be more time-consuming and tedious than with a software package like QM for Windows that is specifically designed for the purpose. A spreadsheet requires that column and row headings for the specific model be set up, and that constraint and objective function formulas be input in their entirety as opposed to just the model parameters as with QM for Windows. However, this is also an advantage of spreadsheets, in that it enables the problem to be set up in an attractive format for reporting and presentation purposes. In addition, once a spreadsheet is set up for one problem, it can often be used as a template for others. Exhibit 1 shows an Excel spreadsheet set up for our Beaver Creek Pottery Company example. An appendix at the end of this text contains a tutorial for "Setting Up and Editing

Exhibit 1

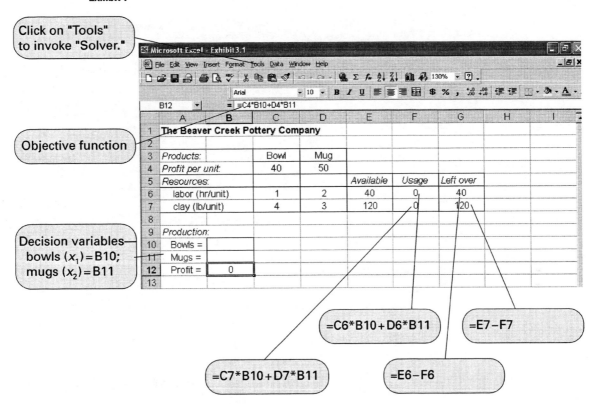

a Spreadsheet" using Exhibit 4 as an example. (Please consult your instructor if you do not have access to and require this appendix.)

The values for bowls and mugs and for profit are contained in cells B10, B11, and B12, respectively. These cells are currently empty because the model has not yet been solved. The objective function for profit, "**=C4*B10+D4*B11,**" is embedded in cell B12 and shown on the formula bar at the top of the screen. This formula is essentially the same as $Z = 40x_1 + 50x_2$ where B10 and B11 represent x_1 and x_2, and B12 equals Z. The objective function coefficients, 40 and 50, are in cells C4 and D4. Similar formulas for the constraints for labor and clay are embedded in cells F6 and F7. For example, in cell F6 we input the formula "**=C6*B10+D6*B11.**"

To solve this problem, first bring down the "Tools" window from the toolbar at the top of the screen and then select "Solver" from the list of menu items. (If "Solver" is not shown on the "Tools" menu, then it can be activated by clicking on "Add-ins" on the "Tools" menu and then "Solver." If Solver is not available from the "Add-ins" menu it must be installed on the "Add-ins" menu directly from the Office or Excel software. For example, in Office you would access "Office set up," then the "Office Applications" menu, then "Excel," then "Add-ins," and then activate "Solver.") The window for "Solver Parameters" will appear as shown in Exhibit 2. Initially all the windows on this screen are blank and we must input the objective function cell, the cells representing the decision variables, and the cells that make up the model constraints.

When inputting the solver parameters as shown in Exhibit 2, we would first input the "target cell" that contains our objective function, which is B12 for our example. (Excel automatically inserts the "$" sign next to cell addresses; you should not type it in.) Next we indicate that we want to maximize the target cell by clicking on "Max." We achieve our objective

Exhibit 2

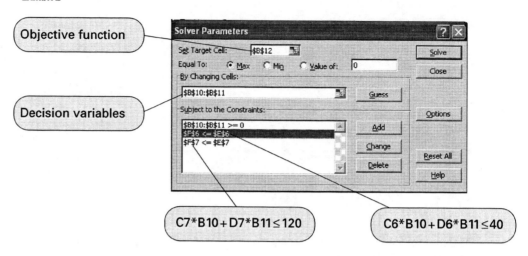

"By Changing Cells" B10 and B11, which represent our model decision variables. The designation "B10:B11" means all the cells between B10 and B11 inclusive. We next input our model constraints by clicking on "Add," which will access the screen shown in Exhibit 3.

Exhibit 3

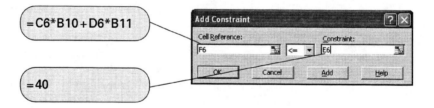

Exhibit 3 shows our labor constraint. Cell F6 contains the constraint formula for labor (=C6*B10+D6*B11), whereas cell E6 contains the labor hours available (i.e., 40). We continue to "Add" constraints until the model is complete. Note that we could have input our constraints by adding a single constraint formula "F6:F7 <= E6:E7," which means that the constraints in cells F6 and F7 are less than or equal to the values in cells E6 and E7, respectively. Notice on the "Solver Parameters" screen that we have also input the nonnegativity constraints for our decision variables, **B10:B11>=0.** This is necessary but it can also be achieved in the "Options" screen as explained next.

Click on "OK." This will return us to the "Solver Parameters" screen. There is one more necessary step before proceeding to solve the problem. Select "Options" from the "Solver Parameters" screen and then when the "Options" screen appears, click on "Assume Linear Models," then "OK." This will ensure that the solver uses the simplex procedure to solve the model and not some other numerical method (which Excel has available). This is not as important for now, but later it will ensure that we get the right reports for sensitivity analysis, a topic we will take up next. Notice that the "Options" screen also enables you to establish the nonnegativity conditions without entering the nonnegativity constraints by clicking on "Assume Non-Negative."

Once the complete model is input, click on "Solve" in the upper right-hand corner of the "Solver Parameters" screen. First, a screen will appear entitled "Solver Results," which will provide you with the opportunity to select the reports you want and then by clicking on "OK" the solution screen shown in Exhibit 4 will appear.

Exhibit 4

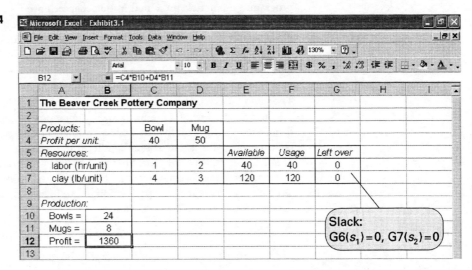

If there had been any extra or "slack" left over for labor or clay, it would have appeared in column G on our spreadsheet under the heading "Left Over." In this case there are no slack resources left over.

We can also generate several reports that summarize the model results. When you click on "OK" from the "Solver" screen, an intermediate screen will appear before the original spreadsheet with the solution results. This screen is entitled "Solver Results" and it provides an opportunity for you to select several reports including the "Answer" report shown in Exhibit 5. This report provides a summary of the solution results.

Exhibit 5

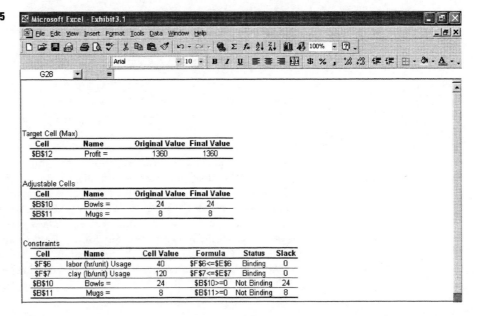

QM for Windows

Before demonstrating how to use QM for Windows we must first make a few comments about the proper form that constraints must be in before a linear programming model can be solved with QM for Windows. The constraints that have been formulated in the linear programming models presented in this chapter have followed a consistent form. All the variables in the constraint have appeared to the left of the inequality, and all numerical values have been on the right-hand side of the inequality. For example, in the fertilizer model the constraint for the nitrogen requirement is

$$2x_1 + 4x_2 \geq 16$$

The value, 16, is referred to as the constraint quantity, or *right-hand-side*, value.

The standard form for a linear programming problem requires constraints to be in this form, with variables on the left side and numerical values to the right of the inequality or equality sign. This is a necessary condition to input problems into some computer programs, and specifically QM for Windows, for linear programming solution.

Consider a model requirement that states that the production of product $3(x_3)$ must be as much as or more than the production of products $1(x_1)$ and $2(x_2)$. The model constraint for this requirement is formulated as

$$x_3 \geq x_1 + x_2$$

This constraint is not in proper form and could not be input into QM for Windows as it is. It must first be converted to

$$x_3 - x_1 - x_2 \geq 0$$

This constraint can now be input for computer solution.

Next consider a problem requirement that the ratio of the production of product $1(x_1)$ to the production of products $2(x_2)$ and $3(x_3)$ must be at least 2 to 1. The model constraint for this requirement is formulated as

$$\frac{x_1}{x_2 + x_3} \geq 2$$

Fractional relationships between variables in constraints must be eliminated.

Although this constraint does meet the condition that variables be on the left side of the inequality and numerical values on the right, it is not in proper form. The fractional relationship of the variables, $x_1/(x_2 + x_3)$, cannot be input into the most commonly used linear programming computer programs in that form. It must be converted to

$$x_1 \geq 2(x_2 + x_3)$$

and

$$x_1 - 2x_2 - 2x_3 \geq 0$$

We will demonstrate how to use QM for Windows by solving our Beaver Creek Pottery Company example. The linear programming module in QM for Windows is accessed by clicking on "Module" at the top of the initial window. This will bring down a window with all the program modules available in QM for Windows. By clicking on "Linear Programming," a window for this program will come up on the screen and by clicking on "File" and then "New," a screen for inputting problem data will appear. Exhibit 6 shows the data screen with all the model parameters for our Beaver Creek Pottery Company example. Notice that we have customized the row headings for "Labor" and "Clay."

Once the model parameters have been input, clicking on "Solve" will result in the model solution as shown in Exhibit 7. It is not necessary to put the model into standard form with slack variables; the program does that for us.

Exhibit 6

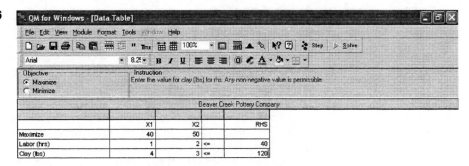

Exhibit 7

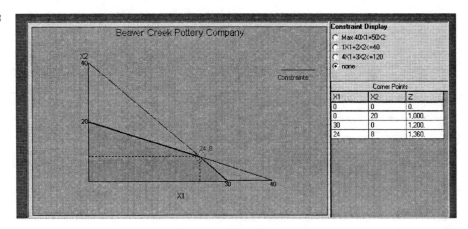

Notice the values 16 and 6 under the column labeled "Dual" for the "Labor" and "Clay" rows. These dual values are the *marginal values* of labor and clay in our problem. This is useful information that is provided in addition to the normal model solution values when you solve a linear programming model. We talk about dual values in more detail later in this chapter, but for now it is sufficient to say that the marginal value is the dollar amount the company would be willing to pay for one additional unit of a resource. For example, the dual value of 16 for the labor constraint means that if one additional hour of labor could be obtained by the company, it would increase profit by $16. Likewise, if one additional pound of clay could be obtained, it would increase profit by $6. Thus, the company would be willing to pay up to $16 for one more hour of labor and $6 for one more pound of clay. The dual value is not the purchase price of one of these resources; it is the maximum amount the company would pay to get more of the resource. These dual values are helpful to the company in making decisions about acquiring additional resources.

QM for Windows will also provide a graphical solution to a linear programming model by clicking on "Window" and then selecting "Graph." Exhibit 8 shows the graphical solution for our Beaver Creek Pottery Company example.

Exhibit 8

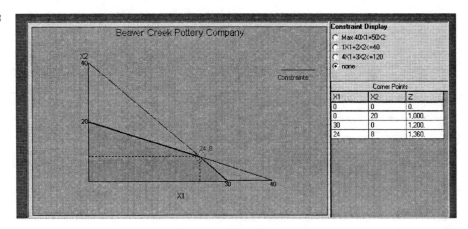

Sensitivity Analysis

Sensitivity analysis *is the analysis of the effect of parameter changes on the optimal solution.*

When linear programming models were formulated in an earlier chapter, it was implicitly assumed that the *parameters* of the model were known with certainty. These parameters include the objective function coefficients, such as profit per bowl; model constraint quantity values, such as available hours of labor; and constraint coefficients, such as pounds of clay per bowl. In the examples presented so far, the models were formulated as if these parameters were known exactly or with certainty. However, rarely does a manager know all of these parameters exactly. In reality the model parameters are simply estimates (or "best guesses") that are subject to change. For this reason it is of interest to the manager to see what effect a change in a parameter will have on the solution to the model. Changes may be either reactions to anticipated uncertainties in the parameters or reactions to information. The analysis of parameter changes and their effects on the model solution is known as *sensitivity analysis*.

The most obvious way to ascertain the effect of a change in the parameter of a model is to make the change in the original model, *resolve* the model, and compare the solution results with the original. However, as we will demonstrate in this chapter, in some cases the effect of changes on the model can be determined without solving the problem again.

Changes in Objective Function Coefficients

The first model parameter change we will analyze is a change in an objective function coefficient. We will use our now-familiar Beaver Creek Pottery Company example to illustrate this change.

$$\text{maximize } Z = \$40x_1 + 50x_2$$
$$\text{subject to}$$
$$x_1 + 2x_2 \le 40 \text{ hr of labor}$$
$$4x_1 + 3x_2 \le 120 \text{ lb of clay}$$
$$x_1, x_2 \ge 0$$

The graphical solution for this problem is shown in Figure 1.

Figure 1
Optimal solution point

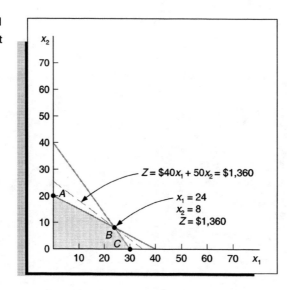

In Figure 1 the optimal solution point is shown to be at point B ($x_1 = 24$ and $x_2 = 8$), which is the last point the objective function, denoted by the dashed line, touches as it leaves the feasible solution area. However, what if we changed the profit of a bowl, x_1, from $40 to $100? How would that affect the solution identified in Figure 1? This change is shown in Figure 2.

Figure 2

Changing the objective function x_1 coefficient

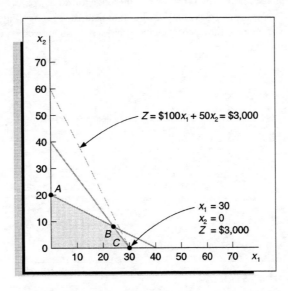

Increasing profit for a bowl (i.e., the x_1 coefficient) from $40 to $100 makes the objective function line steeper, so much so that the optimal solution point changed from point B to point C. Alternatively, if we had increased the profit for a mug, the x_2 coefficient, from $50 to $100, the objective function line would have become flatter, to the extent that point A would become optimal with

$$x_1 = 0, x_2 = 20, \text{ and } Z = \$2,000$$

This is shown in Figure 3.

Figure 3

Changing the objective function x_2 coefficient

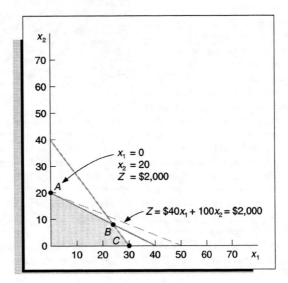

The sensitivity range for an objective coefficient is the range of values over which the current optimal solution point will remain optimal.

The objective of sensitivity analysis in this case is to determine the range of values for a specific objective function coefficient over which the optimal solution point, x_1 and x_2, will remain optimal. For example, the coefficient of x_1 in the objective function is originally \$40, but at some value greater than \$40, point C will become optimal, and at some value less than \$40, point A will become optimal. The focus of sensitivity analysis is to determine those two values, referred to as the sensitivity range for the x_1 coefficient, which we will designate as c_1.

For our simple example we can look at the graph in Figure 1 and determine the sensitivity range for the x_1 coefficient. The slope of the objective function is currently $-4/5$, determined as follows.

$$Z = 40x_1 + 50x_2$$

or

$$50x_2 = Z - 40x_1$$

and

$$x_2 = \frac{Z}{50} - \frac{4x_1}{5}$$

Management Science Application

Grape Juice Management at Welch's

With annual sales over \$550 million, Welch's is one of the world's largest grape-processing companies. Founded in 1869 by Dr. Thomas B. Welch, it processes raw grapes (nearly 300,000 tons per year) into juice, as well as jellies and frozen concentrates. Welch's is owned by the National Grape Cooperative Association (NGCA), which has a membership of 1,400 growers. Welch's is NGCA's production, distribution, and marketing organization. Welch's operates its grape-processing plants near its growers. Because of the dynamic nature of product demand and customer service, Welch's holds finished goods inventory as a buffer, and maintains a large raw materials inventory stored as grape juice in refrigerated tank farms. Packaging operations at each plant draw juice from the tank farms during the year as needed. The value of the stored grape juice often exceeds \$50 million. Harvest yields and grape quality vary between localities. In order to maintain national quality and consistency in its products, Welch's transfers juices between plants and adjusts product recipes. To do this Welch's uses a spreadsheet-based linear programming model. The juice logistics model (JLM) encompasses 324 decision variables and 361 constraints, that minimizes the combined costs of transporting grape juice between plants and the product recipes at each plant, and the carrying cost of storing grape juice. The model decision variables include the grape juice shipped to customers for different product groups, the grape juice transferred between plants, and inventory levels at each plant. Constraints are for recipe requirements, inventories, and grape juice usage and transfers. During the first year the linear

Photo courtesy of Welch Foods Inc.

programming model was used, it saved Welch's between \$130 thousand and \$170 thousand in carrying costs alone by showing Welch's it did not need to purchase extra grapes that were then available. The model has enabled Welch's management to make quick decisions regarding inventories, purchasing grapes, and adjusting product recipes when grape harvests are higher or lower than expected, and when demand changes, resulting in significant cost savings.

Source: E. W. Schuster and S. J. Allen, "Raw Material Management at Welch's, Inc.," *Interfaces* 28, no. 5 (September–October 1998): 13–24.

The objective function is now in the form of the equation of a straight line, $y = a + bx$, where the intercept, a, equals $Z/50$ and the slope, b, is $-4/5$.

If the slope of the objective function increases to $-4/3$, the objective function line becomes exactly parallel to the constraint line,

$$4x_1 + 3x_2 = 120$$

and point C becomes optimal (along with B). The slope of this constraint line is $-4/3$, so we ask ourselves what objective function coefficient for x_1 will make the objective function slope equal $-4/3$? The answer is determined as follows, where c_1 is the objective function coefficient for x_1,

$$\frac{-c_1}{50} = \frac{-4}{3}$$
$$-3c_1 = -200$$
$$c_1 = \$66.67$$

If the coefficient of x_1 is 66.67, then the objective function will have a slope of $-66.67/50$ or $-4/3$. This is illustrated in Figure 4(a).

Figure 4

Determining the sensitivity range for c_1

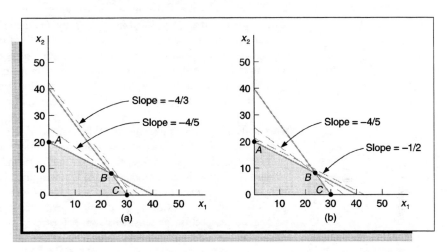

(a)   (b)

We have determined that the upper limit of the sensitivity range for c_1, the x_1 coefficient, is 66.67. If profit for a bowl increases to exactly \$66.67, the solution points will be both B and C. If the profit for a bowl is more than \$66.67, point C will be the optimal solution point.

The lower limit for the sensitivity range can be determined by observing Figure 4(b). In this case, if the objective function line slope decreases (becomes flatter) from $-4/5$ to the same slope as the constraint line,

$$x_1 + 2x_2 = 40$$

then point A becomes optimal (along with B). The slope of this constraint line is $-1/2$, that is, $x_2 = 20 - (1/2)x_1$. In order to have an objective function slope of $-1/2$, the profit for a bowl would have to decrease to \$25, as follows.

$$\frac{-c_1}{50} = \frac{-1}{2}$$
$$-2c_1 = -50$$
$$c_1 = \$25$$

This is the lower limit of the sensitivity range for the x_1 coefficient.

The complete sensitivity range for the x_1 coefficient can be expressed as

$$25 \leq c_1 \leq 66.67$$

This means that the profit for a bowl can vary anywhere between \$25.00 and \$66.67 and the optimal solution point, $x_1 = 24$ and $x_2 = 8$, will not change. Of course, the total profit, or Z value, will change depending on whatever value c_1 actually is.

For the manager this is useful information. Changing the production schedule in terms of how many items are produced can have a number of ramifications in an operation. Packaging, logistical, and marketing requirements for the product might need to be altered. However, with the preceding sensitivity range the manager knows how much the profit, and hence the selling price and costs, can be altered without resulting in a change in production.

Performing the same type of graphical analysis will provide the sensitivity range for the x_2 objective function coefficient, c_2. This range is $30 \leq c_2 \leq 80$. This means that the profit for a mug can vary between \$30 and \$80 and the optimal solution point, B, will not change. However, for this case and the range for c_1, the sensitivity range generally applies only if one coefficient is varied and the other held constant. Thus, when we say that profit for a mug can vary between \$30 and \$80, this is true only if c_1 remains constant.

Simultaneous changes can be made in the objective function coefficients as long as the changes taken together do not change the optimal solution point. However, determining the effect of these simultaneous changes is overly complex and time-consuming using graphical analysis. In fact, graphical analysis is a tedious way to perform sensitivity analysis in general, and it is impossible when the linear programming model contains three or more variables, thus requiring a three-dimensional graph. However, Excel and management science software packages like QM for Windows provide sensitivity analysis for linear programming problems as part of their standard solution output. Determining the effect of simultaneous changes in model parameters and performing sensitivity analysis in general are much easier and more practical using the computer. Later in this chapter we will show the sensitivity analysis output for Excel and QM for Windows.

However, before moving on to computer-generated sensitivity analysis, we want to look at one more aspect of the sensitivity ranges for objective function coefficients. Recall that the model for our fertilizer minimization model is

$$
\begin{aligned}
&\text{minimize } Z = \$6x_1 + 3x_2 \\
&\text{subject to} \\
&\quad 2x_1 + 4x_2 \geq 16 \\
&\quad 4x_1 + 3x_2 \geq 24 \\
&\quad x_1, x_2 \geq 0
\end{aligned}
$$

and the solution shown graphically in Figure 5 is $x_1 = 0, x_2 = 8$, and $Z = 24$.

The sensitivity ranges for the objective function coefficients are

$$4 \leq c_1 \leq \infty$$

$$0 \leq c_2 \leq 4.5$$

Notice that the upper bound for the x_1, coefficient range is "infinity." The reason for this upper limit can be seen in the graphical solution of the problem shown in Figure 5.

As the objective function coefficient for x_1 decreases from \$6, the objective function slope of -2 decreases and the objective function line gets flatter. When the coefficient, c_1, equals \$4, then the slope of the objective function is $-4/3$, which is the same as the constraint line, $4x_1 + 3x_2 = 24$. This makes point B optimal (as well as A). Thus, the lower limit

Figure 5
Fertilizer example: sensitivity range for c_1

x2
14
12
10
8
6
4
2
0
x1 = 0
x2 = 8
Z = $24
A
Slope = −4/3
Slope = −2
B
C
2
4
6
8
10
12
14
x1

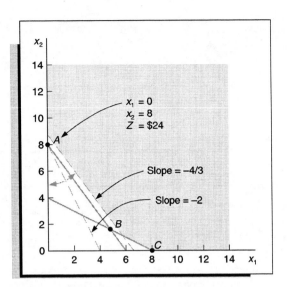

of the sensitivity range for c_1 is \$4. However, notice that as c_1 increases from \$6 the objective function simply becomes steeper and steeper as it rotates toward the x_2 axis of the graph. The objective function will not come into contact with another feasible solution point. Thus, no matter how much we increase cost for Super-gro fertilizer (x_1), point A will always be optimal.

Objective Function Coefficient Ranges with the Computer

When we provided the Excel spreadsheet solution for the Beaver Creek Pottery Company example earlier in this chapter, we did not include sensitivity analysis. However, Excel will also generate a sensitivity report that provides the sensitivity ranges for the objective function coefficients. When you click on "Solve" from the "Solver Parameters" window, you will momentarily go to a "Solver Results" screen shown in Exhibit 9, which provides you with an opportunity to select different reports before proceeding to the solution. This is how we selected our "Answer" report earlier. The sensitivity report for our Beaver Creek Pottery Company example is shown in Exhibit 10. However, note that if you have not already clicked on "Assume Linear Models" from the "Options" screen as we earlier warned, Excel will not generate this version of the sensitivity report.

Exhibit 9

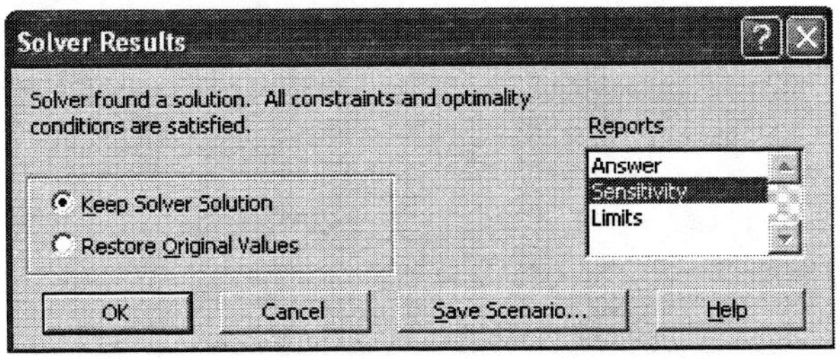

Solver Results
Solver found a solution. All constraints and optimality conditions are satisfied.
Reports
Answer
Sensitivity
Limits
Keep Solver Solution
Restore Original Values
OK
Cancel
Save Scenario...
Help

Notice that the sensitivity ranges for the objective function coefficients (40 and 50) are not provided as an upper and lower limit but instead show an allowable increase and an allowable decrease. For example, for the coefficient of \$40 for bowls (B10), the allowable increase of 26.667 results in an upper limit of 66.667, whereas the allowable decrease of 15 results in a lower limit of 25.

Exhibit 10

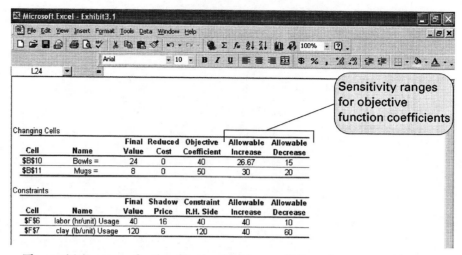

The sensitivity ranges for the objective function coefficients for our example are presented in QM for Windows in Exhibit 11. Notice that this output provides the upper and lower limits of the sensitivity ranges for both variables, x_1 and x_2.

Exhibit 11

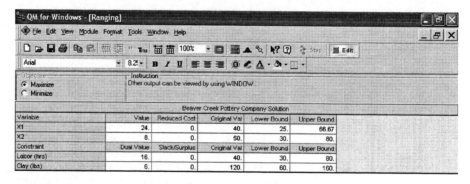

Changes in Constraint Quantity Values

The second type of sensitivity analysis we will discuss is the sensitivity ranges for the constraint quantity values, that is, the values to the right of the inequality signs in the constraints. For our Beaver Creek Pottery Company model,

$$\text{maximize } Z = \$40x_1 + 50x_2$$
$$\text{subject to}$$
$$x_1 + 2x_2 + s_1 = 40 \text{ (labor, hr)}$$
$$4x_1 + 3x_2 + s_2 = 120 \text{ (clay, lb)}$$
$$x_1, x_2 \geq 0$$

the constraint quantity values are 40 and 120.

Consider a change in which the manager of the pottery company can increase the labor hours from 40 to 60. The effect of this change in the model is graphically displayed in Figure 6.

By increasing the available labor hours from 40 to 60, the feasible solution space changed. It was originally OABC and now it is OA'B'C. B' is the new optimal solution instead of B. However, the important consideration in this type of sensitivity analysis is that

Figure 6

Increasing the labor constraint
quantity

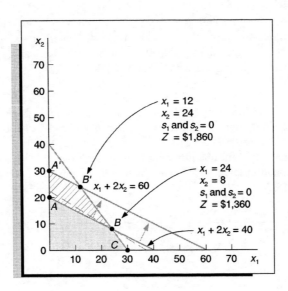

The sensitivity range for a right-hand-side value is the range of values over which the quantity values can change without changing the solution variable mix, including slack variables.

the solution *mix* (or variables that do not have zero values), including slack variables, did not change even though the values of x_1 and x_2 did change (from $x_1 = 24$, $x_2 = 8$ to $x_1 = 12$, $x_2 = 24$). The focus of sensitivity analysis for constraint quantity values is to determine the range over which the constraint quantity values can change without changing the solution variable mix, specifically including the slack variables.

If the quantity value for the labor constraint is increased from 40 to 80 hours, the new solution space is $OA'C$, and a new solution variable mix occurs at A', as shown in Figure 7(a). Whereas at the original optimal point, B, both x_1 and x_2 are in the solution, at the new optimal point, A', only x_2 is produced (i.e., $x_1 = 0$, $x_2 = 40$, $s_1 = 0$, $s_2 = 0$).

Figure 7

Determining the sensitivity
range for labor quantity

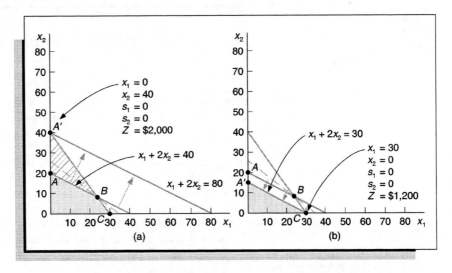

Thus, the upper limit of the sensitivity range for the quantity value for the first constraint, which we will refer to as q_1, is 80 hours. At this value the solution mix changes such that bowls are no longer produced. Furthermore, as q_1 increases past 80 hours, s_1 increases (i.e., slack hours are created). Similarly, if the value for q_1 is decreased to 30 hours, then the new feasible solution space is $OA'C$, as shown in Figure 7(b). The new optimal point is at C, where no mugs (x_2) are produced. The new solution is $x_1 = 30$, $x_2 = 0$, $s_1 = 0$, $s_2 = 0$, and $Z = \$1,200$. Again, the variable mix is changed. Summarizing, the sensitivity range for the constraint quantity value for labor hours is

$$30 \leq q_1 \leq 80 \text{ hr}$$

The sensitivity range for clay can be determined graphically in a similar manner. If the quantity value for the clay constraint, $4x_1 + 3x_2 \leq 120$, is increased from 120 to 160, shown in Figure 8(a), then a new solution space, OAC', results, with a new optimal point, C'. Alternatively, if the quantity value is decreased from 120 to 60, as shown in Figure 8(b), the new solution space is OAC' and the new optimal point is A ($x_1 = 0$, $x_2 = 20$, $s_1 = 0$, $s_2 = 0$, $Z = \$800$).

Figure 8

Determining the sensitivity range for clay quantity

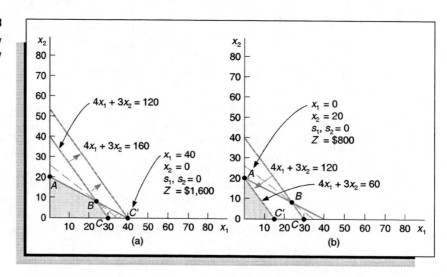

Summarizing, the sensitivity ranges for q_1 and q_2 are

$$30 \leq q_1 \leq 80 \text{ hr}$$

$$60 \leq q_2 \leq 160 \text{ lb}$$

As was the case with the sensitivity ranges for the objective function coefficient, these sensitivity ranges are valid for only one q_i value and assumes all other q_i values are held constant. However, simultaneous changes can occur as long as they do not change the variable mix.

These ranges for constraint quantity values provide useful information for the manager, especially regarding production scheduling and planning. If resources are reduced at the pottery company, then at some point one of the products will no longer be produced and the support facilities and apparatus for that production will not be needed, or extra hours of resources will be created that are not needed. A similar result will occur if resources are increased, albeit a better result, since profit will be more than with a reduction in resources.

Constraint Quantity Value Ranges with the Computer

Previously we showed how to generate the sensitivity report for Excel resulting in Exhibit 10. This report is shown again in Exhibit 12 with the sensitivity ranges for the constraint quantity values highlighted. As we mentioned previously, the ranges are expressed in terms of an allowable increase and decrease instead of upper and lower limits.

Exhibit 12

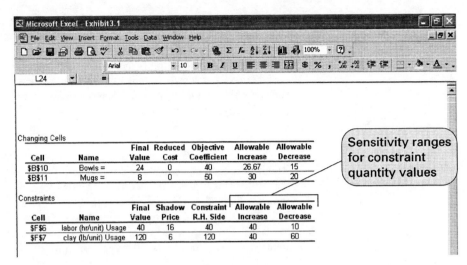

Changing Cells						
Cell	Name	Final Value	Reduced Cost	Objective Coefficient	Allowable Increase	Allowable Decrease
B10	Bowls =	24	0	40	26.67	15
B11	Mugs =	8	0	50	30	20

Constraints						
Cell	Name	Final Value	Shadow Price	Constraint R.H. Side	Allowable Increase	Allowable Decrease
F6	labor (hr/unit) Usage	40	16	40	40	10
F7	clay (lb/unit) Usage	120	6	120	40	60

> **Sensitivity ranges for constraint quantity values**

The sensitivity ranges for the constraint quantity values with QM for Windows can be observed by looking back at Exhibit 11.

Other Forms of Sensitivity Analysis

Other forms of sensitivity analysis include changing constraint parameter values, adding new constraints, and adding new variables.

Excel and QM for Windows provided sensitivity analysis ranges for objective function coefficients and constraint quantity values as part of the standard solution output. However, there are other forms of sensitivity analysis, including changing individual constraint parameters, adding new constraints, and adding new variables.

For instance, in our Beaver Creek Pottery example, if a new less experienced artisan was hired to make pottery, it might take this individual 1.33 hours to produce a bowl instead of 1 hour. Thus, the labor constraint would change from $x_1 + 2x_2 \leq 40$ to $1.33x_1 + 2x_2 \leq 40$. This change is illustrated in Figure 9.

Figure 9

Changing the x_1 coefficient in the labor constraint

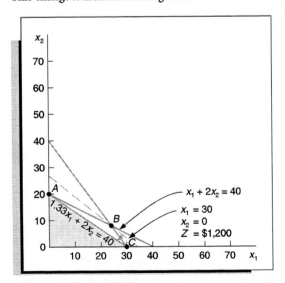

Note that a change in the coefficient for x_1 in the labor constraint rotates the constraint line, changing the solution space from *OABC* to *OAC*. It also results in a new optimal solution point, *C*, where $x_1 = 30$, $x_2 = 0$, and $Z = \$1,200$. Then 1.33 hours would be the logical upper limit for this constraint coefficient. However, as we pointed out, this type of sensitivity analysis for constraint variable coefficients is not typically provided in the standard linear programming computer output. As a result, the most logical way to ascertain the effect of this type of change is simply to run the computer program with different values.

Other types of sensitivity analysis are to add a new constraint to the model or a new variable. For example, suppose the Beaver Creek Pottery Company added a third constraint for packaging its pottery as follows.

$$0.20x_1 + 0.10x_2 \leq 5 \text{ hr}$$

This would require the model to be solved again with the new constraint. This new constraint does, in fact, change the optimal solution, as shown in the Excel spreadsheet in Exhibit 13. This spreadsheet requires a new row (8) added to the original spreadsheet (first shown in Exhibit 4) with our new constraint parameter values, and a new constraint, "F8 ≤ E8", added to the "Solver." In the original model (shown in Exhibit 4) the solution was 24 bowls and 8 mugs with a profit of $1,360. With the new constraint for packaging added, the solution is now 20 bowls and 10 mugs with a profit of $1,300.

Exhibit 13

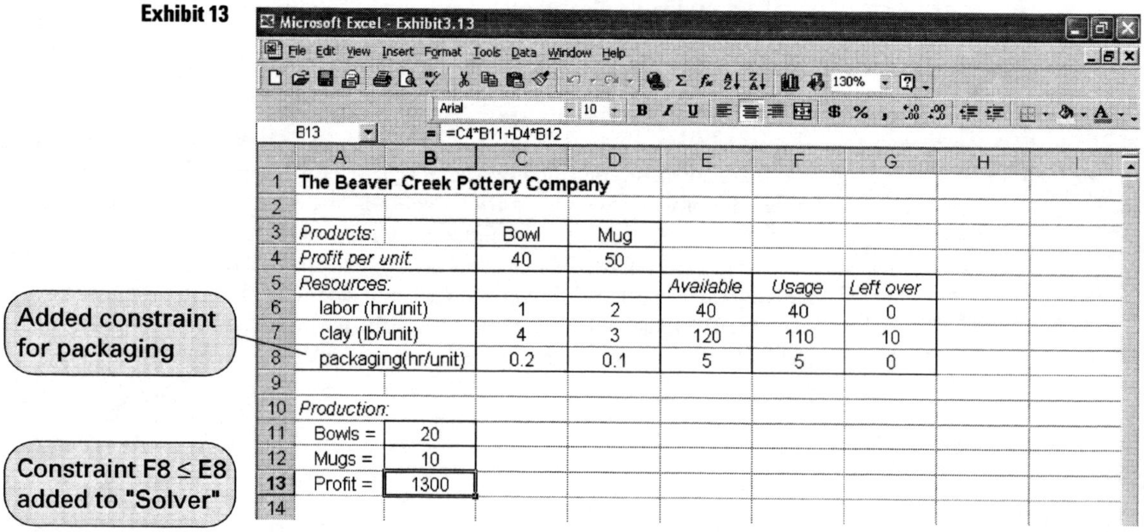

Added constraint for packaging

Constraint F8 ≤ E8 added to "Solver"

If a new variable is added to the model, this would also require that the model be solved again to determine the effect of the change. For example, suppose the pottery company was contemplating producing a third product, cups. It can secure no additional resources, and the profit for a cup is estimated to be $30. This change is reflected in the following model reformulation.

$$\text{maximize } Z = \$40x_1 + 50x_2 + 30x_3$$
$$\text{subject to}$$
$$x_1 + 2x_2 + 1.2x_3 \leq 40 \text{ (labor, hr)}$$
$$4x_1 + 3x_2 + 2x_3 \leq 120 \text{ (clay, lb)}$$
$$x_1, x_2, x_3 \geq 0$$

Solving this new formulation with the computer will show that this prospective change will have no effect on the original solution, that is, the model is not sensitive to this change. The estimated profit from cups was not enough to offset the production of bowls and mugs, and the solution remained the same.

Shadow Prices

We briefly discussed dual values (also called *shadow prices*) earlier in this chapter in our discussion of QM for Windows. You will recall that a dual value was defined as the marginal value of one additional unit of resource. We need to mention shadow prices again at this point in our discussion of sensitivity analysis because decisions are often made regarding resources by considering the marginal value of resources in conjunction with their sensitivity ranges.

Consider again the Excel sensitivity report for the Beaver Creek Pottery Company example shown in Exhibit 14.

Exhibit 14

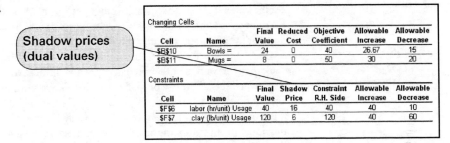

Shadow prices (dual values)

Changing Cells

Cell	Name	Final Value	Reduced Cost	Objective Coefficient	Allowable Increase	Allowable Decrease
B10	Bowls =	24	0	40	26.67	15
B11	Mugs =	8	0	50	30	20

Constraints

Cell	Name	Final Value	Shadow Price	Constraint R.H. Side	Allowable Increase	Allowable Decrease
F6	labor (hr/unit) Usage	40	16	40	40	10
F7	clay (lb/unit) Usage	120	6	120	40	60

The shadow price (or marginal value) for labor is $16 per hour, and the shadow price for clay is $6 per pound. This means that for every additional hour of labor that can be obtained, profit will increase by $16. If the manager of the pottery company could secure more labor at $16 per hour, how much more can be obtained before the optimal solution mix will change and the current shadow price is no longer valid? The answer is at the upper limit of the sensitivity range for the labor constraint value. A maximum of 80 hours of labor can be used before the optimal solution mix changes. Thus, the manager could secure 40 more hours, the allowable increase shown in the Excel sensitivity output for the labor constraint. If 40 extra hours of labor can be obtained, what would its total value be? The answer is ($16/hr)(40 hr) = $640. In other words, profit would be increased by $640 if 40 extra hours of labor could be obtained. This is shown in the Excel output in Exhibit 15 where increasing the labor constraint from 40 to 80 hours has increased profit from $1,360 to $2,000, or $640.

Exhibit 15

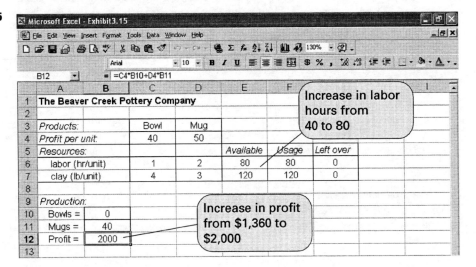

Increase in labor hours from 40 to 80

Increase in profit from $1,360 to $2,000

Alternatively, what would be the effect on profit if one of the Native American artisans was sick one day during the week and the available labor hours decreased from 40 to 32? Profit in this case would decrease by $16 per hour or a total amount of $128. Thus, total profit would fall from $1,360 to $1,232.

Similarly, if the pottery company could obtain only 100 pounds of clay instead of its normal weekly allotment of 120 pounds, what would be the effect on profit? Profit would decrease by $6 per pound for 20 pounds or a total of $120. This would result in an overall reduction in profit from $1,360 to $1,240.

The sensitivity range for a constraint quantity value is also the range over which the shadow price is valid.

Thus, another piece of information that is provided by the sensitivity ranges for the constraint quantity values is the range over which the shadow price remains valid. When q_i increases past the upper limit of the sensitivity range or decreases below the lower limit, the shadow price will change, specifically because slack (or surplus) will be created. Therefore, the sensitivity range for the constraint quantity value is the range over which the shadow price is valid.

The shadow price of $16 for one hour of labor is not necessarily what the manager would *pay* for an hour of labor. This depends on how the objective function is defined. In the Beaver Creek Pottery Company example we are assuming that all of the resources available, 40 hours of labor and 120 pounds of clay, are already paid for. Even if the company does not use all the resources, it still must pay for them. These are *sunk* costs. As such, the individual profit values in the objective function for each product are not affected by how much of a resource is actually used; the total profit is independent of the resources used. In this case the shadow prices are the maximum amounts the manager would pay for additional units of resource. The manager would pay up to $16 for one extra hour of labor and up to $6 for an extra pound of clay.

Alternatively, if each hour of labor and each pound of clay is purchased separately, and thus are not sunk costs, then profit is a function of the cost of the resources. In this case the shadow price would be the additional amount, over and above the original cost of the resource, that would be paid for one more unit of the resource.

Summary

This chapter has focused primarily on the computer solution of linear programming problems. This required us first to show how a linear programming model is put into standard form with the addition of slack variables or the subtraction of surplus variables. Computer solution also enabled us to consider the topic of sensitivity analysis, the analysis of the effect of model parameter changes on the solution of a linear programming model.

References

Baumol, W. J. *Economic Theory and Operations Analysis*. 4th ed. Englewood Cliffs, N.J.: Prentice-Hall, 1977.

Charnes, A., and Cooper, W. W. *Management Models and Industrial Applications of Linear Programming*. New York: John Wiley & Sons, 1961.

Dantzig, G. B. *Linear Programming and Extensions*. Princeton, N.J.: Princeton University Press, 1963.

Gass, S. *Linear Programming*. 4th ed. New York: McGraw-Hill, 1975.

Hadley, G. *Linear Programming*. Reading, Mass.: Addison-Wesley, 1962.

Hillier, F. S., and Lieberman, G. J. *Introduction to Operations Research*. 4th ed. San Francisco: Holden-Day, 1986.

Kwak, N. K. *Mathematical Programming with Business Applications*. New York: McGraw-Hill, 1973.

Llewellyn, R. W. *Linear Programming*. New York: Holt, Rinehart and Winston, 1964.

Taha, H. A. *Operations Research, an Introduction*. 4th ed. New York: Macmillan, 1987.

Wagner, H. M. *Principles of Operations Research*. 2nd ed. Englewood Cliffs, N.J.: Prentice-Hall, 1975.

Example Problem Solution

This example demonstrates the transformation of a linear programming model into standard form, sensitivity analysis, computer solution, and shadow prices.

Problem Statement

The Xecko Tool Company is considering bidding on a job for two airplane wing parts. Each wing part must be processed through three manufacturing stages—stamping, drilling, and finishing—for which the company has limited available hours. The linear programming model to determine the number of part 1 (x_1) and part 2 (x_2) the company should produce in order to maximize its profit is as follows.

$$\text{maximize } Z = \$650x_1 + 910x_2$$

subject to

$$4x_1 + 7.5x_2 \leq 105 \text{ (stamping, hr)}$$
$$6.2x_1 + 4.9x_2 \leq 90 \text{ (drilling, hr)}$$
$$9.1x_1 + 4.1x_2 \leq 110 \text{ (finishing, hr)}$$
$$x_1, x_2 \geq 0$$

A. Solve the model graphically.
B. Indicate how much slack resources are available at the optimal solution point.
C. Determine the sensitivity ranges for the profit for wing part 1 and the stamping hours available.
D. Solve this model using Excel.

Solution

A.

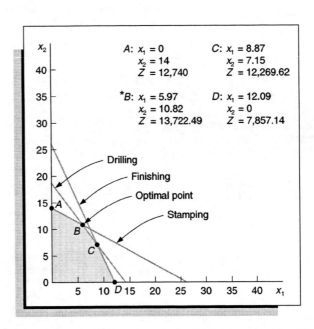

A: $x_1 = 0$
   $x_2 = 14$
   $Z = 12,740$

C: $x_1 = 8.87$
   $x_2 = 7.15$
   $Z = 12,269.62$

*B: $x_1 = 5.97$
   $x_2 = 10.82$
   $Z = 13,722.49$

D: $x_1 = 12.09$
   $x_2 = 0$
   $Z = 7,857.14$

B. The slack at point B where $x_1 = 5.97$ and $x_2 = 10.82$ is computed as follows.

$$4(5.97) + 7.5(10.82) + s_1 = 105 \text{ (stamping, hr)}$$
$$s_1 = 0 \text{ hr}$$
$$6.2(5.97) + 4.9(10.82) + s_2 = 90 \text{ (drilling, hr)}$$
$$s_2 = 0 \text{ hr}$$
$$9.1(5.97) + 4.1(10.82) + s_3 = 110 \text{ (finishing, hr)}$$
$$s_3 = 11.35 \text{ hr}$$

63

C. The sensitivity range for the profit for part 1 is determined by observing the graph of the model and computing how much the slope of the objective function must increase to make the optimal point move from B to C. This is the upper limit of the range and is determined by computing the value of c_1 that will make the slope of the objective function equal with the slope of the constraint line for drilling, $6.2x_1 + 4.9x_2 = 90$.

$$\frac{-c_1}{910} = \frac{-6.2}{4.9}$$
$$c_1 = 1,151.43$$

The lower limit is determined by computing the value of c_1 that will equate the slope of the objective function with the slope of the constraint line for stamping, $4x_1 + 7.5x_2 = 105$.

$$\frac{-c_1}{910} = \frac{-4}{7.5}$$
$$c_1 = 485.33$$

Summarizing,

$$485.33 \leq c_1 \leq 1,151.43$$

The upper limit of the range for stamping hours is determined by first computing the value for q_1 that would move the solution point from B to where the drilling constraint intersects with the x_2 axis where $x_1 = 0$ and $x_2 = 18.37$:

$$4(0) + 7.5(18.37) = q_1$$
$$q_1 = 137.76$$

The lower limit of the sensitivity range occurs where the optimal point B moves to C where $x_1 = 8.87$ and $x_2 = 7.15$:

$$4(8.87) + 7.5(7.15) = q_1$$
$$q_1 = 89.10$$

Summarizing, $89.10 \leq q_1 \leq 137.76$.

D. The Excel spreadsheet solution to this example problem is shown as follows.

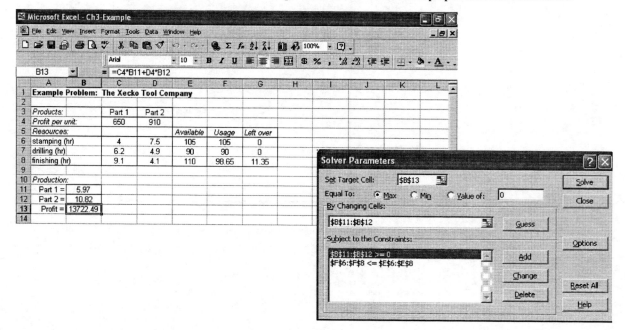

Problems

1. Given the following QM for Windows computer solution of a linear programming model, graph the problem and identify the solution point, including variable values and slack, from the computer output.

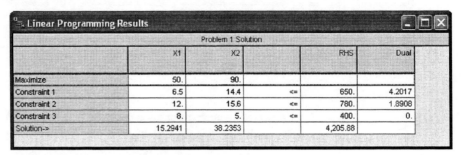

Linear Programming Results						
Problem 1 Solution						
	X1	X2			RHS	Dual
Maximize	50.	90.				
Constraint 1	6.5	14.4	<=		650.	4.2017
Constraint 2	12.	15.6	<=		780.	1.8908
Constraint 3	8.	5.	<=		400.	0.
Solution->	15.2941	38.2353			4,205.88	

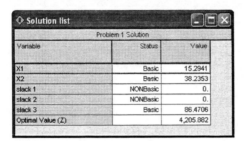

Solution list		
Problem 1 Solution		
Variable	Status	Value
X1	Basic	15.2941
X2	Basic	38.2353
slack 1	NONBasic	0.
slack 2	NONBasic	0.
slack 3	Basic	86.4706
Optimal Value (Z)		4,205.882

2. Explain the primary differences between a software package like QM for Windows and Excel spreadsheets for solving linear programming problems.

3. Given the following Excel spreadsheet for a linear programming model and "Solver" window, indicate the formula for cell B13 and fill in the "Solver" window with the appropriate information to solve the problem.

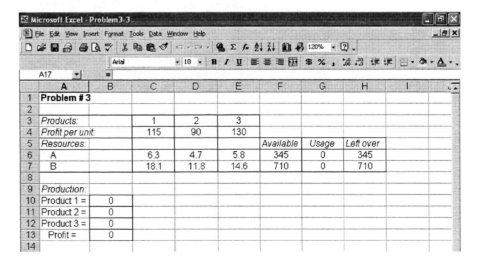

	A	B	C	D	E	F	G	H
1	Problem # 3							
2								
3	Products:		1	2	3			
4	Profit per unit:		115	90	130			
5	Resources:					Available	Usage	Left over
6	A		6.3	4.7	5.8	345	0	345
7	B		18.1	11.8	14.6	710	0	710
8								
9	Production:							
10	Product 1 =	0						
11	Product 2 =	0						
12	Product 3 =	0						
13	Profit =	0						
14								

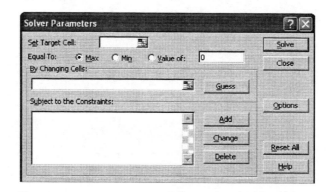

4. Given the following graph of a linear programming model with a single constraint and an objective function maximize $Z = 30x_1 + 50x_2$, determine the optimal solution point.

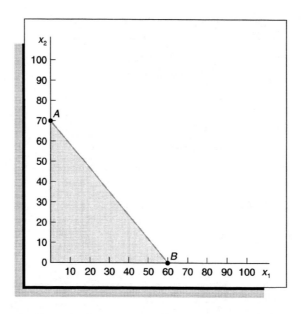

Determine the values that c_1 and c_2 must decrease or increase in order to change the current solution point to the other extreme point.

5. The Southern Sporting Goods Company makes basketballs and footballs. Each product is produced from two resources—rubber and leather. The resource requirements for each product and the total resources available are as follows.

Product	Resource Requirements per Unit	
	Rubber (lb)	Leather (ft²)
Basketball	3	4
Football	2	5
Total resources available	500 lb	800 ft²

Each basketball produced results in a profit of $12, and each football earns $16 in profit.
   a. Formulate a linear programming model to determine the number of basketballs and footballs to produce in order to maximize profit.
   b. Transform this model into standard form.

6. Solve the model formulated in problem 5 for the Southern Sporting Goods Company graphically.
   a. Identify the amount of unused resources (i.e., slack) at each of the graphical extreme points.
   b. What would be the effect on the optimal solution if the profit for a basketball changed from $12 to $13? What would be the effect if the profit for a football changed from $16 to $15?
   c. What would be the effect on the optimal solution if 500 additional pounds of rubber could be obtained? What would be the effect if 500 additional square feet of leather could be obtained?

7. For the linear programming model for the Southern Sporting Goods Company, formulated in problem 5 and solved graphically in problem 6:
   a. Determine the sensitivity ranges for the objective function coefficients and constraint quantity values using graphical analysis.
   b. Verify the sensitivity ranges determined in (a) using the computer.
   c. Using the computer, determine the shadow prices for the resources and explain their meaning.

8. A company produces two products, A and B, which have profits of $9 and $7, respectively. Each unit of product must be processed on two assembly lines, where the required production times are as follows.

| Product | hr/Unit | |
	Line 1	Line 2
A	12	4
B	4	8
Total hours	60	40

   a. Formulate a linear programming model to determine the optimal product mix that will maximize profit.
   b. Transform this model into standard form.

9. Solve problem 8 graphically.
   a. Identify the amount of unused resources (i.e., slack) at each of the graphical extreme points.
   b. What would be the effect on the optimal solution if the production time on line 1 were reduced to 40 hours?
   c. What would be the effect on the optimal solution if the profit for product B were increased from $7 to $15? To $20?

10. For the linear programming model formulated in problem 8 and solved graphically in problem 9:
   a. Determine the sensitivity ranges for the objective function coefficients using graphical analysis.
   b. Verify the sensitivity ranges determined in (a) using the computer.
   c. Using the computer, determine the shadow prices for additional hours of production time on line 1 and line 2, and indicate whether the company would prefer additional line 1 or line 2 hours.

11. Irwin Textile Mills produces two types of cotton cloth—denim and corduroy. Corduroy is a heavier grade of cotton cloth and, as such, requires 7.5 pounds of raw cotton per yard, whereas denim requires 5 pounds of raw cotton per yard. A yard of corduroy requires 3.2 hours of processing time; a yard of denim requires 3.0 hours. Although the demand for denim is practically unlimited, the maximum demand for corduroy is 510 yards per month. The manufacturer has 6,500 pounds of cotton and 3,000 hours of processing time available each month. The manufacturer makes a profit of $2.25 per yard of denim and $3.10 per yard of corduroy. The manufacturer wants to know how many yards of each type of cloth to produce to maximize profit.
    a. Formulate a linear programming model for this problem.
    b. Transform this model into standard form.

12. Solve the model formulated in problem 11 for the Irwin Textile Mills graphically.
    a. How much extra cotton and processing time are left over at the optimal solution? Is the demand for corduroy met?
    b. What is the effect on the optimal solution if the profit per yard of denim is increased from $2.25 to $3.00? What is the effect if the profit per yard of corduroy is increased from $3.10 to $4.00?
    c. What will be the effect on the optimal solution if Irwin Mills could obtain only 6,000 pounds of cotton per month?

13. Solve the linear programming model formulated in problem 11 for Irwin Mills using the computer.
    a. If Irwin Mills can obtain additional cotton or processing time, but not both, which should it select? How much? Explain your answer.
    b. Identify the sensitivity ranges for the objective function coefficients and for the constraint quantity values. Then explain the sensitivity range for the demand for corduroy.

14. The United Aluminum Company of Cincinnati produces three grades (high, medium, and low) of aluminum at two mills. Each mill has a different production capacity (in tons per day) for each grade, as follows.

Aluminum Grade	Mill	
	1	2
High	6	2
Medium	2	2
Low	4	10

The company has contracted with a manufacturing firm to supply at least 12 tons of high-grade aluminum, 8 tons of medium-grade aluminum, and 5 tons of low-grade aluminum. It costs United $6,000 per day to operate mill 1 and $7,000 per day to operate mill 2. The company wants to know the number of days to operate each mill in order to meet the contract at the minimum cost.

Formulate a linear programming model for this problem.

15. Solve the linear programming model formulated in problem 14 for United Aluminum Company graphically.
    a. How much extra (i.e., surplus) high-, medium-, and low-grade aluminum does the company produce at the optimal solution?
    b. What would the effect be on the optimal solution if the cost of operating mill 1 increased from $6,000 to $7,500 per day?

    c. What would the effect be on the optimal solution if the company could supply only 10 tons of high-grade aluminum?

16. Solve the linear programming model formulated in problem 14 for the United Aluminum Company using the computer.
    a. Identify and explain the shadow prices for each of the aluminum grade contract requirements.
    b. Identify the sensitivity ranges for the objective function coefficients and the constraint quantity values.
    c. Would the solution values change if the contract requirements for high-grade aluminum were increased from 12 tons to 20 tons? If yes, what would the new solution values be?

17. The Bradley family owns 410 acres of farmland in North Carolina on which they grow corn and tobacco. Each acre of corn costs $105 to plant, cultivate, and harvest; each acre of tobacco costs $210. The Bradleys have a budget of $52,500 for next year. The government limits the number of acres of tobacco that can be planted to 100. The profit from each acre of corn is $300; the profit from each acre of tobacco is $520. The Bradleys want to know how many acres of each crop to plant in order to maximize their profit.

Formulate a linear programming model for this problem.

18. Solve the linear programming model formulated in problem 17 for the Bradley family farm graphically.
    a. How many acres of farmland will not be cultivated at the optimal solution? Do the Bradleys use the entire 100-acre tobacco allotment?
    b. What would the profit for corn have to be for the Bradleys to plant only corn?
    c. If the Bradleys can obtain an additional 100 acres of land, will the number of acres of corn and tobacco they plan to grow change?
    d. If they decide not to cultivate a 50-acre section as part of a crop recovery program, how will it affect their crop plans?

19. Solve the linear programming model formulated in problem 17 for the Bradley farm using the computer.
    a. The Bradleys have an opportunity to lease some extra land from a neighbor. The neighbor is offering the land to them for $110 per acre. Should the Bradleys lease the land at that price? What is the maximum price the Bradleys should pay their neighbor for the land, and how much should they lease at that price?
    b. The Bradleys are considering taking out a loan to increase their budget. For each dollar they borrow, how much additional profit would they make? If they borrowed an additional $1,000, would the number of acres of corn and tobacco they plant change?

20. The manager of a Burger Doodle franchise wants to determine how many sausage biscuits and ham biscuits to prepare each morning for breakfast customers. Each type of biscuit requires the following resources.

Biscuit	Labor (hr)	Sausage (lb)	Ham (lb)	Flour (lb)
Sausage	0.010	0.10	—	0.04
Ham	0.024	—	0.15	0.04

The franchise has 6 hours of labor available each morning. The manager has a contract with a local grocer for 30 pounds of sausage and 30 pounds of ham each morning. The manager also purchases

16 pounds of flour. The profit for a sausage biscuit is $0.60; the profit for a ham biscuit is $0.50. The manager wants to know the number of each type of biscuit to prepare each morning in order to maximize profit.

Formulate a linear programming model for this problem.

21. Solve the linear programming model formulated in problem 20 for the Burger Doodle restaurant graphically.
    a. How much extra sausage and ham are left over at the optimal solution point? Is there any idle labor time?
    b. What would the solution be if the profit for a ham biscuit were increased from $0.50 to $0.60?
    c. What would be the effect on the optimal solution if the manager could obtain 2 more pounds of flour?

22. Solve the linear programming model developed in problem 20 for the Burger Doodle restaurant using the computer.
    a. Identify and explain the shadow prices for each of the resource constraints.
    b. Which of the resources constrain profit the most?
    c. Identify the sensitivity ranges for the profit of a sausage biscuit and the amount of sausage available. Explain these sensitivity ranges.

23. Rucklehouse Public Relations has been contracted to do a survey following an election primary in New Hampshire. The firm must assign interviewers to conduct the survey by telephone or in person. One person can conduct 80 telephone interviews or 40 personal interviews in a single day. The following criteria have been established by the firm to ensure a representative survey.
    ▪ At least 3,000 interviews must be conducted.
    ▪ At least 1,000 interviews must be by telephone.
    ▪ At least 800 interviews must be personal.

An interviewer conducts only one type of interview each day. The cost is $50 per day for a telephone interviewer and $70 per day for a personal interviewer. The firm wants to know the minimum number of interviewers to hire in order to minimize the total cost of the survey.

Formulate a linear programming model for this problem.

24. Solve the linear programming model formulated in problem 23 for Rucklehouse Public Relations graphically.
    a. Determine the sensitivity ranges for the daily cost of a telephone interviewer and the number of personal interviews required.
    b. Does the firm conduct any more telephone and personal interviews than are required, and if so, how many more?
    c. What would be the effect on the optimal solution if the firm were required by the client to increase the number of personal interviews conducted from 800 to a total of 1,200?

25. Solve the linear programming model formulated in problem 23 for Rucklehouse Public Relations using the computer.
    a. If the firm could reduce the minimum interview requirement for either telephone or personal interviews, which should the firm select? How much would a reduction of one interview in the requirement you selected reduce total cost? Solve the model again using the computer with the reduction of this one interview in the constraint requirement to verify your answer.
    b. Identify the sensitivity ranges for the cost of a personal interview and the number of total interviews required.

26. The Bluegrass Distillery produces custom-blended whiskey. A particular blend consists of rye and bourbon whiskey. The company has received an order for a minimum of 400 gallons of the custom blend. The customer specified that the order must contain at least 40% rye and not more than 250 gallons of bourbon. The customer also specified that the blend should be mixed in the ratio of two parts rye to one part bourbon. The distillery can produce 500 gallons per week regardless of the blend. The production manager wants to complete the order in one week. The blend is sold for $5 per gallon.

    The distillery company's cost per gallon is $2 for rye and $1 for bourbon. The company wants to determine the blend mix that will meet customer requirements and maximize profits.

    Formulate a linear programming model for this problem.

27. Solve the linear programming model formulated in problem 26 for the Bluegrass Distillery graphically.
    a. Indicate the slack and surplus available at the optimal solution point and explain their meanings.
    b. What increase in the objective function coefficients in this model would change the optimal solution point? Explain your answer.

28. Solve the linear programming model formulated in problem 26 for the Bluegrass Distillery using the computer.
    a. Identify the sensitivity ranges for the objective function coefficients and explain what the upper and lower limits are.
    b. How much would it be worth to the distillery to obtain additional production capacity?
    c. If the customer decided to change the blend requirement for its custom-made whiskey to a mix of three parts rye to one part bourbon, how would this change the optimal solution?

29. Alexis Harrington received an inheritance of $95,000, and she is considering two speculative investments—the purchase of land and the purchase of cattle. Each investment would be for one year. Under the present (normal) economic conditions, each dollar invested in land will return the principal plus 20% of the principal; each dollar invested in cattle will return the principal plus 30%. However, both investments are relatively risky. If economic conditions were to deteriorate, there is an 18% chance she would lose everything she invested in land and a 30% chance she would lose everything she invested in cattle. Alexis does not want to lose more than $20,000 (on average). She wants to know how much to invest in each alternative to maximize the cash value of the investments at the end of one year.

    Formulate a linear programming model for this problem.

30. Solve the linear programming model formulated in problem 29 for Alexis Harrington graphically.
    a. How much would the return for cattle have to increase in order for Alexis to invest only in cattle?
    b. Should all of Alexis's inheritance be invested according to the optimal solution?
    c. How much "profit" would the optimal solution earn Alexis over and above her investment?

31. Solve the linear programming model formulated in problem 29 for Alexis Harrington using the computer.
    a. If Alexis decided to invest some of her own savings along with the money from her inheritance, what return would she realize for each dollar of her own money that she invests? How much of her own savings could she invest before this return would change?
    b. If the risk of losing the investment in land increased to 30%, how would this change the optimal investment mix?

LINEAR PROGRAMMING: COMPUTER SOLUTION AND SENSITIVITY ANALYSIS

32. Transform the following linear programming model into standard form and solve using the computer.

$$\text{maximize } Z = 140x_1 + 205x_2 + 190x_3$$

subject to

$$10x_1 + 15x_2 + 8x_3 \le 610$$

$$\frac{x_1}{x_2} \le 3$$

$$x_1 \ge 0.4\,(x_1 + x_2 + x_3)$$

$$x_2 \ge x_3$$

$$x_1, x_2, x_3 \ge 0$$

33. Chemco Corporation produces a chemical mixture for a specific customer in 1,000-pound batches. The mixture contains three ingredients—zinc, mercury, and potassium. The mixture must conform to formula specifications that are supplied by the customer. The company wants to know the amount of each ingredient it needs to put in the mixture that will meet all the requirements of the mix and minimize total cost.

The customer has supplied the following formula specifications for each batch of mixture.
- The mixture must contain at least 200 pounds of mercury.
- The mixture must contain at least 300 pounds of zinc.
- The mixture must contain at least 100 pounds of potassium.
- The ratio of potassium to the other two ingredients cannot exceed 1 to 4.

The cost per pound of mercury is $400; the cost per pound of zinc, $180; and the cost per pound of potassium, $90.
   a. Formulate a linear programming model for this problem.
   b. Solve the model formulated in (a) using the computer.

34. The following linear programming model formulation is used for the production of four different products, with two different manufacturing processes and two different material requirements.

$$\text{maximize } Z = \$50x_1 + 58x_2 + 46x_3 + 62x_4$$

subject to

$$4x_1 + 3.5x_2 + 4.6x_3 + 3.9x_4 \le 600 \text{ hr (process 1)}$$

$$2.1x_1 + 2.6x_2 + 3.5x_3 + 1.9x_4 \le 500 \text{ hr (process 2)}$$

$$15x_1 + 23x_2 + 18x_3 + 25x_4 \le 3,600 \text{ lb (material A)}$$

$$8x_1 + 12.6x_2 + 9.7x_3 + 10.5x_4 \le 1,700 \text{ lb (material B)}$$

$$\frac{x_1 + x_2}{x_1 + x_2 + x_3 + x_4} \ge .60$$

$$x_1, x_2, x_3, x_4 \ge 0$$

   a. Solve this problem using the computer.
   b. Identify the sensitivity ranges for the objective function coefficients and the constraint quantity values.
   c. Which is the most valuable resource to the firm?
   d. One of the four products is not produced in the optimal solution. How much would the profit for this product have to be for it to be produced?

72

35. The Island Publishing Company publishes two types of magazines on a monthly basis, a restaurant and entertainment guide and a real estate guide. The company distributes the magazines free to businesses, hotels, and stores on Hilton Head Island in South Carolina. The company's profits come exclusively from the paid advertising in the magazines. Each of the restaurant and entertainment guides distributed generates $0.50 per magazine in advertising revenue, whereas the real estate guide generates $0.75 per magazine. The real estate magazine is a more sophisticated publication that includes color photos and accordingly it costs $0.25 per magazine to print, compared with only $0.17 for the restaurant and entertainment guide. The publishing company has a printing budget of $4,000 per month. There is enough rack space to distribute at most 18,000 magazines each month. In order to entice businesses to place advertisements, Island Publishing promises to distribute at least 8,000 copies of each magazine. The company wants to determine the number of copies of each magazine it should print each month in order to maximize advertising revenue.

    Formulate a linear programming model for this problem.

36. Solve the linear programming model formulation in problem 35 for the Island Publishing Company graphically.
    a. Determine the sensitivity range for the advertising revenue generated by the real estate guide.
    b. Does the company spend all of its printing budget? If not, how much slack is left over?
    c. What would be the effect on the optimal solution if the local real estate agents insisted that 12,000 copies of the real estate guide be distributed instead of the current 8,000 copies or they would withdraw their advertising?

37. Solve the linear programming model formulated in problem 35 for the Island Publishing Company using the computer.
    a. How much would it be worth to the Island Publishing Company to obtain enough additional rack space to distribute 18,500 copies instead of the current 18,000 copies? 20,000 copies?
    b. How much would it be worth to Island Publishing to reduce the requirement to distribute the entertainment guide from 8,000 to 7,000 copies?

38. Mega-Mart, a discount store chain, is to build a new store in Rock Springs. The parcel of land the company has purchased is large enough to accommodate a store with 140,000 square feet of floor space. Based on marketing and demographic surveys of the area and historical data from its other stores, Mega-Mart estimates its annual profit per square foot for each of the store's departments to be as shown in the following table.

Department	Profit per ft^2
Men's clothing	$4.25
Women's clothing	5.10
Children's clothing	4.50
Toys	5.20
Housewares	4.10
Electronics	4.90
Auto supplies	3.80

Each department must have at least 15,000 ft^2 of floor space and no department can have more than 20% of the total retail floor space. Men's, women's, and children's clothing plus housewares keep all their stock on the retail floor; however, toys, electronics, and auto supplies keep some items (like bicycles, televisions, and tires) in inventory. Thus, 10% of the total retail floor space devoted to these three departments must be set aside outside the retail area for stocking inventory. Mega-Mart wants to know the floor space that should be devoted to each department in order to maximize profit.

    a. Formulate a linear programming model for this problem.

    b. Solve this model using the computer.

39.   a. In problem 38 Mega-Mart is considering purchasing a parcel of land adjacent to the current site it plans to build its store on. The cost of the parcel is $190,000 and it would enable Mega-Mart to increase the size of its store to 160,000 ft^2. Discuss whether Mega-Mart should purchase the land and increase the planned size of the store.

    b. Suppose that the profit per ft^2 will decline in all departments by 20% if the store size increases to 160,000 ft^2. (If the stock does not turn over as fast, increasing inventory costs will reduce profit.) How might this affect Mega-Mart's decision in (a)?

40. The Food Max grocery store sells three brands of milk in half-gallon cartons—its own brand, a local dairy brand, and a national brand. The profit from its own brand is $0.97 per carton, the profit from the local dairy brand is $0.83 per carton, and the profit from the national brand is $0.69 per carton. The total refrigerated shelf space allotted to half-gallon cartons of milk is 36 square feet per week. A half-gallon carton takes up 16 square inches of shelf space. The store manager knows that each week Food Max always sells more of the national brand than the local dairy brand and its own brand combined and at least three times as much of the national brand as its own brand. In addition, the local dairy can supply only 10 dozen cartons per week. The store manager wants to know how many half-gallon cartons of each brand to stock each week in order to maximize profit.

    a. Formulate a linear programming model for this problem.

    b. Solve this model using the computer.

41.   a. If Food Max in problem 40 could increase its shelf space for half-gallon cartons of milk, how much would profit increase per carton?

    b. If Food Max could get the local dairy to increase the amount of milk it could supply each week, would it increase profit?

    c. Food Max is considering discounting its own brand in order to increase sales. If it were to do so it would decrease the profit margin for its own brand to $0.86 per carton, but it would cut the demand for the national brand relative to its own brand in half. Discuss whether the store should implement the price discount.

42. John Hoke owns Hoke's Spokes, a bicycle shop. Most of John's bicycle sales are customer orders; however, he also stocks bicycles for walk-in customers. He stocks three types of bicycles—road-racing, cross-country, and mountain. A road-racing bike costs $1,200, a cross-country bike costs $1,700, and a mountain bike costs $900. He sells road-racing bikes for $1,800, cross-country bikes for $2,100, and mountain bikes for $1,200. He has $12,000 available this month to purchase bikes. Each bike must be assembled; a road-racing bike requires 8 hours to assemble, a cross-country bike requires 12 hours, and a mountain bike requires 16 hours. He estimates that he and his employees have 120 hours available to assemble bikes. He has enough space in his store to order 20 bikes this month. Based on past sales, John wants to stock at least twice as many mountain bikes as the other two combined because mountain bikes sell better.

Formulate a linear programming model for this problem.

43. Solve the linear programming model formulated in problem 42 for Hoke's Spokes using the computer.

    a. Should John Hoke try to increase his budget for purchasing bikes, increase space to stock bikes, or increase labor hours to assemble bikes? Why?

b. If John were to hire an additional worker for 30 hours at $10 per hour, how much additional profit would he make, if any?

c. If John were to purchase a cheaper cross-country bike for $1,200 and sell it for $1,900, would it affect the original solution?

44. The Metro Food Services Company delivers fresh sandwiches each morning to vending machines throughout the city. The company makes three kinds of sandwiches—ham and cheese, bologna, and chicken salad. A ham and cheese sandwich requires a worker 0.45 minutes to assemble, a bologna sandwich requires 0.41 minutes, and a chicken salad sandwich requires 0.50 minutes to make. The company has 960 available minutes each night for sandwich assembly. Vending machine capacity is available for 2,000 sandwiches each day. The profit for a ham and cheese sandwich is $0.35, the profit for a bologna sandwich is $0.42, and the profit for a chicken salad sandwich is $0.37. The company knows from past sales records that their customers buy as many or more of the ham and cheese sandwiches than the other two sandwiches combined, but customers need a variety of sandwiches available, so Metro stocks at least 200 of each. Metro management wants to know how many of each sandwich it should stock to maximize profit.

Formulate a linear programming model for this problem.

45. Solve the linear programming problem formulated in problem 44 for the Metro Food Services Company using the computer.

a. If Metro Food Services could hire another worker and increase its available assembly time by 480 minutes, or increase its vending machine capacity by 100 sandwiches, which should it do? Why? How much additional profit would your decision result in?

b. What would the effect be on the optimal solution if the requirement that at least 200 sandwiches of each kind be stocked were eliminated? Compare the profit between the optimal solution and this solution, and indicate which solution you would recommended.

c. What would the effect be on the optimal solution if the profit for a ham and cheese sandwich were increased to $0.40? $0.45?

46. Mountain Laurel Vineyards produces three kinds of wine—Mountain Blanc, Mountain Red, and Mountain Blush. The company has 17 tons of grapes available to produce wine this season. A cask of Blanc requires 0.21 tons of grapes, a cask of Red requires 0.24 tons, and a cask of Blush requires 0.18 tons. The vineyard has enough storage space in its aging room to store 80 casks of wine.

The vineyard has 2,500 hours of production capacity and it requires 12 hours to produce a cask of Blanc, 14.5 hours to produce a cask of Red, and 16 hours to produce a cask of Blush. From past sales the vineyard knows that demand for the Blush will be no more than half of the sales of the other two wines combined. The profit for a cask of Blanc is $7,500, the profit for a cask of Red is $8,200, and the profit for a cask of Blush is $10,500.

Formulate a linear programming model for this problem.

47. Solve the linear programming model formulated in problem 46 for Mountain Laurel Vineyards using the computer.

a. If the vineyard were to determine that the profit from Red was $7,600 instead of $8,200, how would that affect the optimal solution?

b. If the vineyard could secure one additional unit of any of the resources used in the production of wine, which one should it select?

c. If the vineyard could obtain 0.5 more tons of grapes, 500 more hours of production capacity, or enough storage capacity to store 4 more casks of wine, which should it choose?

d. All three wines are produced in the optimal solution. How little would the profit for Blanc have to be for it to no longer be produced?

48. Exeter Mines produces iron ore at four different mines; however, the ores extracted at each mine are different in their iron content. Mine 1 produces magnetic ore, which has a 70% iron content; mine 2 produces limonite ore, which has a 60% iron content; mine 3 produces pyrite ore, which has a 50% iron content; and mine 4 produces taconite ore, which has only a 30% iron content. Exeter has three customers that produce steel—Armco, Best, and Corcom. Armco needs 400 tons of pure (100%) iron, Best requires 250 tons of pure iron, and Corcom requires 290 tons. It costs $37 to extract and process one ton of magnetite ore at mine 1, $46 to produce a ton of limonite ore at mine 2, $50 per ton of pyrite ore at mine 3, and $42 per ton of taconite ore at mine 4. Exeter can extract 350 tons of ore at mine 1, 530 tons at mine 2, 610 tons at mine 3, and 490 tons at mine 4. The company wants to know how much ore to produce at each mine in order to minimize cost and meet its customers' demand for pure (100%) iron.

Formulate a linear programming model for this problem

49. Solve the linear programming problem formulated in problem 48 for Exeter Mines using the computer.
    a. Do any of the mines have slack capacity? If yes, which one(s)?
    b. If Exeter Mines could increase production capacity at any one of its mines, which should it be? Why?
    c. If Exeter were to decide to increase capacity at the mine identified in (b), how much could it increase capacity before the optimal solution point (i.e., the optimal set of variables) would change?
    d. If Exeter were to determine it could increase production capacity at mine 1 from 350 tons to 500 tons at an increase in production costs to $43 per ton, should it do so?

50. Given the following linear programming model,

$$\text{minimize } Z = 8.2x_1 + 7.0x_2 + 6.5x_3 + 9.0x_4$$
$$\text{subject to}$$
$$6x_1 + 2x_2 + 5x_3 + 7x_4 \geq 820$$
$$\frac{x_1}{x_1 + x_2 + x_3 + x_4} \geq .3$$
$$\frac{x_2 + x_3}{x_1 + x_4} \leq .2$$
$$x_3 \geq x_1 + x_4$$
$$x_1, x_2, x_3, x_4 \geq 0$$

Transform the model into standard form and solve using the computer.

MOSAIC TILES, LTD.

Gilbert Moss and Angela Pasaic spent several summers during their college years working at archaeological sites in the Southwest. While at these digs, they learned how to make ceramic tiles from local artisans. After college they made use of their college experiences to start a tile manufacturing firm called Mossaic Tiles, Ltd. They opened their plant in New Mexico, where they would have convenient access to a special clay they intend to use to make a clay derivative for their tiles. Their manufacturing operation consists of a few relatively simple but precarious steps, including molding the tiles, baking, and glazing.

Gilbert and Angela plan to produce two basic types of tile for use in home bathrooms, kitchens, sunrooms, and laundry rooms. The two types of tile are a larger, single-colored tile and a smaller, patterned tile. In the manufacturing process the color or pattern is added before a tile is glazed. Either a single color is sprayed over the top of a baked set of tiles or a stenciled pattern is sprayed on the top of a baked set of tiles.

The tiles are produced in batches of 100. The first step is to pour the clay derivative into specially constructed molds. It takes 18 minutes to mold a batch of 100 larger tiles and 15 minutes to prepare a mold for a batch of 100 smaller tiles. The company has 60 hours available each week for molding. After the tiles are molded they are baked in a kiln: 0.27 hour for a batch of 100 larger tiles and 0.58 hour for a batch of 100 smaller tiles. The company has 105 hours available each week for baking. After baking, the tiles are either colored or patterned and glazed. This process takes 0.16 hour for a batch of 100 larger tiles and 0.20 hour for a batch of 100 smaller tiles. Forty hours are available each week for the glazing process. Each batch of 100 large tiles requires 32.8 pounds of the clay derivative to produce, whereas each batch of smaller tiles requires 20 pounds. The company has 6,000 pounds of the clay derivative available each week.

Mossaic Tiles earns a profit of $190 for each batch of 100 of the larger tiles and $240 for each batch of 100 smaller patterned tiles. Angela and Gilbert want to know how many batches of each type of tile to produce each week to maximize profit. In addition, they also have some questions about resource usage they would like answered.

A. Formulate a linear programming model for Mossaic Tiles, Ltd. and determine the mix of the tiles it should manufacture each week.
B. Transform the model into standard form.
C. Solve the linear programming model graphically.
D. Determine the resources left over and not used at the optimal solution point.
E. Determine the sensitivity ranges for the objective function coefficients and constraint quantity values using the graphical solution of the model.
F. For artistic reasons Gilbert and Angela like to produce the smaller, patterned tiles better. They also believe in the long run the smaller tiles will be a more successful product. What must the profit be for the smaller tiles in order for the company to produce only the smaller tiles?
G. Solve the linear programming model using the computer and verify the sensitivity ranges computed in (E).
H. Mossaic believes it may be able to reduce the time required for molding to 16 minutes for a batch of larger tiles and 12 minutes for a batch of the smaller tiles. How will this affect the solution?
I. The company that provides Mossaic with clay has indicated that it can deliver an additional 100 pounds each week. Should Mossaic agree to this offer?
J. Mossaic is considering adding capacity to one of its kilns to provide 20 additional glazing hours per week at a cost of $90,000. Should it make the investment?
K. The kiln for glazing had to be shut down for 3 hours, reducing the available kiln hours from 40 to 37. What effect will this have on the solution?

"THE POSSIBILITY" RESTAURANT—CONTINUED

In "The Possibility" Restaurant case problem presented earlier, Angela Fox and Zooey Caulfield opened a French restaurant called "The Possibility." Initially, Angela and Zooey could not offer a full, varied menu, so their chef, Pierre, prepared two full-course dinners with beef and fish each evening. In the case problem, Angela and Zooey wanted to develop a linear programming model to help them determine the number of beef and fish meals they should prepare each night. Solve Zooey and Angela's linear programming model using the computer.

A. Angela and Zooey are considering investing in some advertising to increase the maximum number of meals they serve. They estimate that if they spend $30 per day on a newspaper ad it will increase the maximum number of meals they serve per day from 60 to 70. Should they make the investment?
B. Zooey and Angela are also concerned about the reliability of some of their kitchen staff. They estimate that on some

evenings they could have a staff reduction of as much as five hours. How would this affect their profit level?

C. The final question they would like to explore is raising the price of the fish dinner. Angela believes the price for a fish dinner is a little low and that it could be closer to the price of a beef dinner without affecting customer demand. How-

ever, Zooey has noted that Pierre has already made plans based on the number of dinners recommended by the linear programming solution. Angela has suggested a price increase that will increase profit for the fish dinner to $14. Would this be acceptable to Pierre, and how much additional profit would be realized?

CASE PROBLEM

JULIA'S FOOD BOOTH

Julia Robertson is a senior at Tech and she's investigating different ways to finance her final year at school. She is considering leasing a food booth outside the Tech stadium at home football games. Tech sells out every home game and Julia knows, from attending the games herself, that everyone eats a lot of food. She has to pay $1,000 per game for a booth and the booths are not very large. Vendors can sell either food or drinks on Tech property, but not both. Only the Tech athletic department concession stands can sell both inside the stadium. She thinks slices of cheese pizza, hot dogs, and barbecue sandwiches are the most popular food items among fans and so these are the items she would sell.

Most food items are sold during the hour before the game starts and during half time; thus it will not be possible for Julia to prepare the food while she is selling it. She must prepare the food ahead of time and then store it in a warming oven. For $600 she can lease a warming oven for the six-game home season. The oven has 16 shelves and each shelf is 3 feet by 4 feet. She plans to fill the oven with the three food items before the game and then again before half time.

Julia has negotiated with a local pizza delivery company to deliver 14-inch cheese pizzas twice each game—two hours before the game and right after the opening kickoff. Each pizza will cost her $6 and will include 8 slices. She estimates it will cost her $0.45 for each hot dog and $0.90 for each barbecue sandwich if she makes the barbecue herself the night before. She measured a hot dog and found it takes up about 16 in² of space, whereas a barbecue sandwich takes up about 25 in². She plans to sell a slice of pizza and a hot dog for $1.50 apiece and a barbecue sandwich for $2.25. She has $1,500 in cash available to purchase and prepare the food items for the first home game; for the remaining five games she will purchase her ingredients with money she has made from the previous game.

Julia has talked to some students and vendors who have sold food at previous football games at Tech as well as at other universities. From this she has discovered that she can expect to sell at least as many slices of pizza as hot dogs and barbecue sandwiches combined. She also anticipates that she will probably sell at least twice as many hot dogs as barbecue sandwiches. She believes that she will sell everything she can stock and develop a customer base for the season if she follows these general guidelines for demand.

If Julia clears at least $1,000 in profit for each game after paying all her expenses she believes it will be worth leasing the booth.

A. Formulate and solve a linear programming model for Julia that will help you advise her if she should lease the booth.

B. If Julia were to borrow some more money from a friend before the first game to purchase more ingredients, could she increase her profit? If so, how much should she borrow and how much additional profit would she make? What factor constrains her from borrowing even more money than this amount (indicated in your answer to the previous question)?

C. When Julia looked at the solution in (A) she realized that it would be physically difficult for her to prepare all the hot dogs and barbecue sandwiches indicated in this solution. She believes she can hire a friend of hers to help her for $100 per game. Based on the results in (A) and (B), is this something you think she could reasonably do and should do?

D. Julia seems to be basing her analysis on the assumption that everything will go as she plans. What are some of the uncertain factors in the model that could go wrong and adversely affect Julia's analysis? Given these uncertainties and the results in (A), (B), and (C) what do you recommend that Julia do?

Solutions to Selected Odd-Numbered Problems

3. Cells: B10:B12; Constraints: B10:B12 $\geq$ 0, G6 $\leq$ F6, G7 $\leq$ F7; Profit: $= $ B10*C4+B11*D4+B12*E4

5. (a and b) max. $Z = 12x_1 + 16x_2 + 0s_1 + 0s_2$; s.t. $3x_1 + 2x_2 + s_1 = 500$, $4x_1 + 5x_2 + s_2 = 800, x_i \geq 0, s_i \geq 0$

7. (a and b) $\infty < c_1, < 12.8, 15 < c_2 < \infty, 320 \leq q_1 \leq \infty$, $0 \leq q_2 \leq 1,250$; (c) $0, $3.20

9. (a) $x_1 = 4, x_2 = 3, Z = 57$, A: $s_1 = 40, s_2 = 0$, B: $s_1 = 0, s_2 = 0$, C: $s_1 = 0$, $s_2 = 20$; (b) $x_1 = 2, x_2 = 4$; (c) solution point same for profit = $15, new solution $x_1 = 0, x_2 = 5, Z = 100$ for profit = $20

11. (a and b) max. $Z = 2.25x_1 + 3.10x_2 + 0s_1 + 0s_2 + 0s_3$; s.t. $5.0x_1 + 7.5x_2 + s_1 = 6,500, 3.0x_1 + 3.2x_2 + s_2 = 3,000, x_2 + s_3 = 510, x_i \geq 0$, $s_j \geq 0$

13. (a) Additional processing time, $0.75/hr; (b) $0 < c_1 \leq 2.906, 2.4 < c_2 < \infty, 6,105 \leq q_1 \leq \infty, 1,632 \leq q_2 \leq 3,237, 0 \leq q_3 \leq 692.308$

15. (a) $x_1 = 4, x_2 = 0, s_1 = 0, s_2 = 0, s_3 = 11, Z = 24,000$; (b) $x_1 = 1, x_2 = 3, Z = 28,500$; (c) B still optimal, $x_1 = 0.5, x_2 = 3.5, Z = 27,500$

17. (a and b) max. $Z = 300x_1 + 520x_2 + 0s_1 + 0s_2 + 0s_3$; s.t. $x_1 + x_2 + s_1 = 410, 105x_1 + 210x_2 + s_2 = 52,500, x_2 + s_3 = 100, x_i \geq 0, s_j \geq 0$

19. (a) no, max. price = $80; (b) $2.095

21. (a) $x_1 = 300, x_2 = 100, s_1 = 0$ lb, $s_2 = 15$ lb, $s_4 = 0.6$ hr, $Z = 230$; (b) $c_1 = $0.60, x_1 = 257, x_2 = 143, Z = 225.70$; (c) $x_1 = 300, x_2 = 125$, $Z = 242.50$

23. (a and b) min. $Z = 50x_1 + 70x_2 + 0s_1 + 0s_2 + 0s_3$; s.t. $80x_1 + 40x_2 - s_1 = 3,000, 80x_1 - s_2 = 1,000, 40x_2 - s_3 = 800, x_i, s_j \geq 0$

25. (a) personal interviews, $0.625/interview; (b) $25 < c_2 < \infty$, $1,800 \leq q_1 \leq \infty$

27. (a) $x_1 = 333.3, x_2 = 166.7, s_1 = 100$ gal, $s_2 = 133.3$ gal, $s_3 = 83.3$ gal, $s_4 = 100$ gal, $Z = 1,666$; (b) any values of c

29. (a and b) max. $Z = 1.20x_1 + 1.30x_2$; s.t. $x_1 + x_2 \leq 95,000, .18x_1 + .30x_2 \leq 20,000, x_i \geq 0$

31. (a) 5%, $16,111.11; (b) $x_1 = 0, x_2 = 66,666.7, Z = 86,666.67$

33. (a and b) min. $Z = 400x_1 + 180x_2 + 90x_3$ s.t. $x_1 \geq 200, x_2 \geq 300, x_3 \geq 100, 4x_3 - x_1 - x_2 \leq 0, x_1 + x_2 + x_3 = 1,000, x_i \geq 0$; (c) $x_1 = 200, x_2 = 600, x_3 = 200, Z = 206,000$

35. (a) max. $Z = 0.50x_1 + 0.75x_2$; s.t. $0.17x_1 + 0.25x_2 \leq 4,000, x_1 + x_2 \leq 18,000, x_1 \geq 8,000, x_2 \geq 8,000, x_1, x_2 \geq 0$; (b) max. $Z = 0.50x_1 + 0.75x_2 + 0S_1 + 0S_2 + 0S_3; 0.17x_1 + 0.25x_2 + s_1 = 4,000, x_1 + x_2 + s_2 = 18,000, x_1 - s_3 = 8,000, x_2 - s_4 = 8,000, x_i \geq 0, s_i \geq 0$

37. $x_1 = 8,000, x_2 = 10,000, Z = 11,500$; (a) $375; increase, $x_1 = 8,000$, $x_2 = 10,500, Z = $11,875; x_1 = 8,000, x_2 = 10,560, Z = $11,920$

39. (a) purchase land; (b) not purchase land

41. (a) $0.78, 360 cartons; (b) $0; (c) $x_1 = 108, x_2 = 54, x_3 = 162, Z = 249.48$, no discount

43. $x_1 = 3, x_3 = 6, Z = 3,600$; (a) more assembly hr; (b) additional profit = $600; (c) no effect

45. $x_1 = 1,000, x_2 = 800, x_3 = 200, Z = 760$; (a) increase by 100, $38 in additional profit; (b) $x_1 = 1,000, x_2 = 1,000, Z = 770$; (c) $Z = 810; x_1 = 1,600 x_2 = 200, x_3 = 200$

47. $x_1 = 5.3, x_2 = 4.7, Z = 806$

49. (a) 12 hr; (b) new solution $- x_1 = 5.09, x_2 = 5.45, Z = 111.27$

3

Transportation, Transshipment, and Assignment Problems

The Transportation Model

TIMEOUT for Frank L. Hitchcock and Tjalling C. Koopmans

Management Science Application: Transporting Sand for Airport Construction Landfill

Computer Solution of a Transportation Problem

Computer Solution with Excel • Computer Solution with Excel QM • QM for Windows Solution

The Transshipment Model

Computer Solution with Excel

The Assignment Model

Computer Solution of the Assignment Problem

Computer Solution with Excel • Computer Solution with QM for Windows

Management Science Application: Assigning Managers to Construction Projects

Summary · References · Example Problem Solution · Problems · Case Problems

Ⅰn this chapter, we examine three special types of linear programming model formulations—*transportation, transshipment,* and *assignment problems.* They are part of a larger class of linear programming problems known as *network flow problems.* We are considering these problems in a separate chapter because they represent a popular group of linear programming applications.

These problems have special mathematical characteristics that enabled management scientists to develop very efficient, unique mathematical solution approaches to them. These solution approaches were variations of the traditional simplex solution procedure. However, like the simplex method we have placed these detailed manual, mathematical solution procedures—called the *transportation method* and *assignment method*—on the CD that accompanies this text. We will focus on model formulation and solution with the computer, specifically Excel and QM for Windows.

The Transportation Model

In a **transportation problem,** *items are allocated from sources to destinations at a minimum cost.*

The transportation model is formulated for a class of problems with the following unique characteristics: (1) A product is *transported* from a number of sources to a number of destinations at the minimum possible cost; and (2) each source is able to supply a fixed number of units of the product, and each destination has a fixed demand for the product. Although the general transportation model can be applied to a wide variety of problems, it is this particular application to the transportation of goods that is most familiar and from which the problem draws its name.

The following example will demonstrate the formulation of the transportation model. Wheat is harvested in the Midwest and stored in grain elevators in three different cities—Kansas City, Omaha, and Des Moines. These grain elevators supply three flour mills, located in Chicago, St. Louis, and Cincinnati. Grain is shipped to the mills in railroad cars, each car capable of holding one ton of wheat. Each grain elevator is able to supply the following number of tons (i.e., railroad cars) of wheat to the mills on a monthly basis.

Grain Elevator	Supply
1. Kansas City	150
2. Omaha	175
3. Des Moines	<u>275</u>
Total	600 tons

Each mill demands the following number of tons of wheat per month.

Mill	Demand
A. Chicago	200
B. St. Louis	100
C. Cincinnati	<u>300</u>
Total	600 tons

The cost of transporting one ton of wheat from each grain elevator (source) to each mill (destination) differs according to the distance and rail system. These costs are shown in the following table. For example, the cost of shipping one ton of wheat from the grain elevator at Omaha to the mill at Chicago is $7.

	Mill		
Grain Elevator	A. Chicago	B. St. Louis	C. Cincinnati
1. Kansas City	$6	$ 8	$10
2. Omaha	7	11	11
3. Des Moines	4	5	12

The linear programming model for a transportation problem has constraints for supply at each source and demand at each destination.

The problem is to determine how many tons of wheat to transport from each grain elevator to each mill on a monthly basis to minimize the total cost of transportation. A diagram of the different transportation routes with supply, demand, and cost figures is given in Figure 1.

Figure 1

Network of transportation routes for wheat shipments

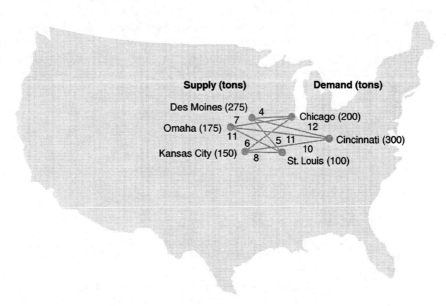

The linear programming model for this problem is formulated in the equations that follow.

minimize $Z = \$6x_{1A} + 8x_{1B} + 10x_{1C} + 7x_{2A} + 11x_{2B} + 11x_{2C} + 4x_{3A} + 5x_{3B} + 12x_{3C}$
subject to

$$x_{1A} + x_{1B} + x_{1C} = 150$$
$$x_{2A} + x_{2B} + x_{2C} = 175$$
$$x_{3A} + x_{3B} + x_{3C} = 275$$
$$x_{1A} + x_{2A} + x_{3A} = 200$$
$$x_{1B} + x_{2B} + x_{3B} = 100$$
$$x_{1C} + x_{2C} + x_{3C} = 300$$
$$x_{ij} \geq 0$$

In this model the decision variables, x_{ij}, represent the number of tons of wheat transported from each grain elevator, i (where $i = 1, 2, 3$), to each mill, j (where $j = $ A, B, C). The objective function represents the total transportation cost for each route. Each term in the objective function reflects the cost of the tonnage transported for one route. For example, if

20 tons are transported from elevator 1 to mill A, the cost of $6 is multiplied by x_{1A} ($= 20$), which equals $120.

The first three constraints in the linear programming model represent the supply at each elevator; the last three constraints represent the demand at each mill. As an example, consider the first supply constraint, $x_{1A} + x_{1B} + x_{1C} = 150$. This constraint represents the tons of wheat transported from Kansas City to all three mills: Chicago (x_{1A}), St. Louis (x_{1B}), and Cincinnati (x_{1C}). The amount transported from Kansas City is limited to the 150 tons available. Note that this constraint (as well as all others) is an equation ($=$) rather than a $\leq$ inequality because all of the tons of wheat available will be needed to meet the *total demand* of 600 tons. In other words, the three mills demand 600 total tons, which is the exact amount that can be supplied by the three grain elevators. Thus, all that *can* be supplied *will be*, in order to meet demand. This type of model, in which supply exactly equals demand, is referred to as a *balanced transportation model*.

In a **balanced transportation** *model in which supply equals demand, all constraints are equalities.*

In an **unbalanced transportation model** *supply is greater than demand or demand is greater than supply.*

Realistically, however, an *unbalanced problem* in which supply exceeds demand or demand exceeds supply is a more likely occurrence. In our wheat transportation example, if the demand at Cincinnati is increased from 300 tons to 350 tons, a situation is created in which total demand is 650 tons and total supply is 600 tons. This would result in the following change in our linear programming model of this problem.

$$\text{minimize } Z = 6x_{1A} + 8x_{1B} + 10x_{1C} + 7x_{2A} + 11x_{2B} + 11x_{2C} + 4x_{3A} + 5x_{3B} + 12x_{3C}$$
subject to
$$x_{1A} + x_{1B} + x_{1C} = 150$$
$$x_{2A} + x_{2B} + x_{2C} = 175$$
$$x_{3A} + x_{3B} + x_{3C} = 275$$
$$x_{1A} + x_{2A} + x_{3A} \leq 350$$
$$x_{1B} + x_{2B} + x_{3B} \leq 100$$
$$x_{1C} + x_{2C} + x_{3C} \leq 300$$
$$x_{ij} \geq 0$$

One of the demand constraints will not be met because there is not enough total supply to meet total demand. If, instead, supply exceeds demand, then the supply constraints would be $\leq$.

Sometimes one or more of the routes in the transportation model may be *prohibited*. That is, units cannot be transported from a particular source to a particular destination. When this situation occurs we must make sure that the variable representing this route does not have a value in the optimal solution. This can be accomplished by assigning a very large relative cost as the coefficient of this prohibited variable in the objective function. For example, in our wheat-shipping example, if the route from Kansas City to Chicago is prohibited (perhaps because of a rail strike). Then the variable x_{1A} is given a coefficient of "100" instead of "6" in the objective function, so x_{1A} will equal zero in the optimal solution because of its high relative cost.

Time Out for Frank L. Hitchcock and Tjalling C. Koopmans

Several years before George Dantzig formalized the linear programming technique, Frank L. Hitchcock in 1941 formulated the transportation problem as a method for supplying a product from several factories to a number of cities given varying freight rates. In 1947 T. C. Koopmans independently formulated the same type of problem. Koopmans, an American economist originally from the Netherlands and a professor at Chicago and Yale, was awarded the Nobel Prize in 1975.

Management Science Application

Transporting Sand for Airport Construction Landfill

During the construction of the Brisbane (Australia) International Airport, approximately 1,800,000 cubic meters of sand were dredged from a nearby bay and transported to 26 temporary sites near the airport. Once the sand had settled and drained, it was transported to 35 final landfill sites around the airport. A transportation model was used to determine the optimal amount of sand to ship from the different temporary sites to the various landfill locations on a monthly basis. The objective of the model was to minimize the product of distance and volume of sand moved. The difference in the initial cost estimate and the cost derived from using the transportation model was a savings of over $800,000.

Photo courtesy of Australian Consulate General

Source: M. Lawrence and C. Perry, "Earthmoving on Construction Projects: A Postscript," *Interfaces* 14, no. 2 (March–April 1984): 84–86.

Computer Solution of a Transportation Problem

Because the transportation problem is formulated as a linear programming model, it can be solved with Excel and using the linear programming module of QM for Windows that you may have seen in other chapters. However, management science packages such as QM for Windows also have transportation modules that enable problems to be input in a special transportation tableau format. We will first demonstrate solution of the wheat-shipping problem solved earlier in this chapter using Excel spreadsheets.

Computer Solution with Excel

We will first demonstrate how to solve a transportation problem using Excel. Excel does not include a "transportation" module specifically designed to solve transportation problems as does QM for Windows. Instead a transportation problem must be solved in Excel as a linear programming model using the "Solver." Exhibit 1 shows a spreadsheet setup to solve our wheat-shipping example. Notice that the objective function formula for total cost is contained in cell C10 and is shown on the formula bar at the top of the spreadsheet. Cells **G5:G7** in column G and cells **C9:E9** in row 9 labeled "Grain Shipped" contain the constraint formulas for supply and demand, respectively. For example, the constraint formula in cell G7 for the grain shipped from Des Moines to the three mills is "**=C7+D7+E7**" and the right-hand-side quantity value of 275 available tons is in cell F7. The decision variables are contained in cells **C5:E7**.

Exhibit 2 shows the "Solver Parameters" screen for our example. Cell C10 containing the objective function formula is minimized. The constraint formula "**C9:E9=C8:E8**" includes all three demand constraints, and the constraint formula "**G5:G7=F5:F7**" includes all three supply constraints. Before solving this problem, remember to click on "Options" and then on the resulting screen click on "Assume Linear Model" to invoke the linear programming solution approach.

Exhibit 1

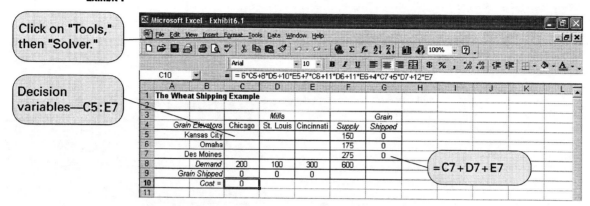

Exhibit 2

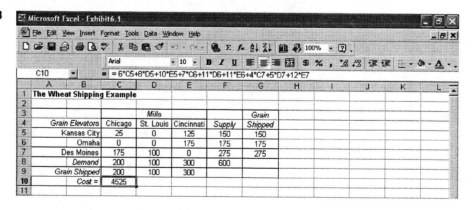

Exhibit 3 shows the optimal solution with the amounts shipped from sources to destinations and the total cost.

Exhibit 3

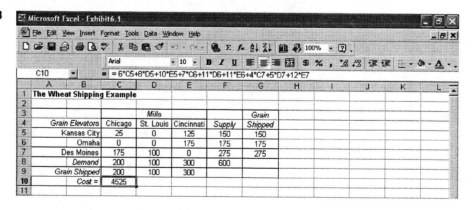

Computer Solution with Excel QM

Excel QM includes a spreadsheet macro for transportation problems. Recall that when Excel QM is activated "QM" is shown on the menu bar at the top of the spreadsheet. Clicking on "QM" and then selecting "Transportation" will result in the "Spreadsheet

Initialization" window shown in Exhibit 4. In this window we set the number of sources (i.e., origins) and destinations to 3, selected "Minimize" as the objective, and typed in the title for our example. To exit this window we click on "OK" and the spreadsheet shown in Exhibit 5 is displayed. The transportation problem is completely set up as shown with all the necessary formulas already in the cells. However, initially the data values in cells **B10:E13** are empty; the spreadsheet in Exhibit 5 includes these values that we have typed in.

Exhibit 4

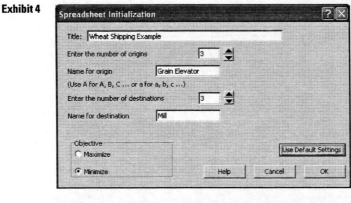

Exhibit 5

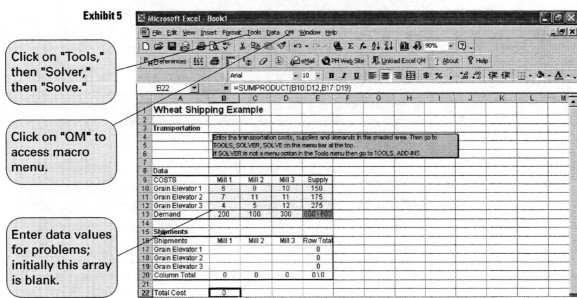

Click on "Tools," then "Solver," then "Solve."

Click on "QM" to access macro menu.

Enter data values for problems; initially this array is blank.

To solve the problem we follow the instructions in the box superimposed on the spreadsheet—click on "Tools" at the top of the spreadsheet, then click on "Solver," and when the "Solver" appears click on "Solve." We have not shown the "Solver" here; however, it is very similar to the one shown in Exhibit 2. It already includes all the decision variables and constraints required to solve the problem; thus, all that is needed is to click on "Solve." The spreadsheet with the solution is shown in Exhibit 6. You will notice that although the total cost is the same as the solution we obtained with Excel in Exhibit 3, the decision variable values in cells **B17:D19** are different. This is because this problem has multiple optimal solutions and this is the alternate solution to the one we got previously.

Exhibit 6

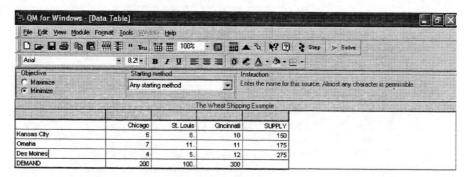

Note: The Exhibit 6 spreadsheet shows a Microsoft Excel window titled "Wheat Shipping Example" with the following data:

Cell B22 = =SUMPRODUCT(B10:D12,B17:D19)

	A	B	C	D	E
1	Wheat Shipping Example				
3	Transportation				
4-6		Enter the transportation costs, supplies and demands in the shaded area. Then go to TOOLS, SOLVER, SOLVE on the menu bar at the top. If SOLVER is not a menu option in the Tools menu then go to TOOLS, ADD-INS.			
8	Data				
9	COSTS	Mill 1	Mill 2	Mill 3	Supply
10	Grain Elevator 1	6	8	10	150
11	Grain Elevator 2	7	11	11	175
12	Grain Elevator 3	4	5	12	275
13	Demand	200	100	300	600 \ 600
15	Shipments				
16	Shipments	Mill 1	Mill 2	Mill 3	Row Total
17	Grain Elevator 1	0	0	150	150
18	Grain Elevator 2	25	0	150	175
19	Grain Elevator 3	175	100	0	275
20	Column Total	200	100	300	600 \ 600
22	Total Cost	4525			

QM for Windows Solution

To access the transportation module for QM for Windows, click on "Module" at the top of the screen and then click on "Transportation." Once you are in the transportation module, click on "File" and then "New" to input the problem data. QM for Windows allows for any of three initial solution methods—northwest corner, minimum cell cost, or VAM—to be selected. These are the three starting solution procedures used in the mathematical procedure for solving transportation problems. Because these techniques are not included in the text (but are included on the accompanying CD), it makes no difference which starting procedure we use. For this example, we selected the minimum cell cost method. Exhibit 7 shows the input data for our wheat-shipping example.

Exhibit 7

Note: The Exhibit 7 window shows QM for Windows - [Data Table] with the following data for "The Wheat Shipping Example":

	Chicago	St. Louis	Cincinnati	SUPPLY
Kansas City	6	8.	10	150
Omaha	7	11.	11	175
Des Moines	4	5.	12	275
DEMAND	200	100.	300	

Once the data are input, clicking on "Solve" at the top of the screen will generate the solution as shown in Exhibit 8. You will notice that QM for Windows will indicate if multiple optimal solutions exist, but it will not identify alternate solutions. This is the same optimal solution that we achieved earlier in our Excel solution.

QM for Windows will provide additional solution reports from the "Windows" menu, including a solution summary in Exhibit 9.

Exhibit 8

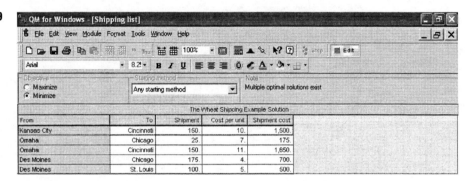

Transportation Shipments			
The Wheat Shipping Example Solution			
Optimal cost = $4,525	Chicago	St. Louis	Cincinnati
Kansas City			150.
Omaha	25.		150.
Des Moines	175.	100.	

Exhibit 9

QM for Windows - [Shipping list]				
File Edit View Module Format Tools Window Help				

Objective: ○ Maximize ● Minimize

Starting method: Any starting method

Note: Multiple optimal solutions exist

The Wheat Shipping Example Solution				
From	To	Shipment	Cost per unit	Shipment cost
Kansas City	Cincinnati	150.	10.	1,500.
Omaha	Chicago	25.	7.	175.
Omaha	Cincinnati	150.	11.	1,650.
Des Moines	Chicago	175.	4.	700.
Des Moines	St. Louis	100.	5.	500.

The Transshipment Model

The transshipment model is an extension of the transportation model in which intermediate transshipment points are added between the sources and destinations. An example of a transshipment point is a distribution center or warehouse located between plants and stores. In a transshipment problem, items may be transported from sources through transshipment points on to destinations, from one source to another, from one transshipment point to another, from one destination to another, or directly from sources to destinations, or some combination of these alternatives.

We will expand our wheat-shipping example to demonstrate the formulation of a transshipment model. Wheat is harvested at farms in Nebraska and Colorado before being shipped to the three grain elevators in Kansas City, Omaha, and Des Moines, which are now transshipment points. The amount of wheat harvested at each farm is 300 tons. The wheat is then shipped to the mills in Chicago, St. Louis, and Cincinnati. The shipping costs from the grain elevators to the mills remain the same, and the shipping costs from the farms to the grain elevators are as follows.

Farm	Grain Elevator		
	3. KANSAS CITY	4. OMAHA	5. DES MOINES
1. Nebraska	$16	10	12
2. Colorado	15	14	17

The basic structure of this model is shown in the graphical network in Figure 2.

Figure 2

Network of transshipment
routes

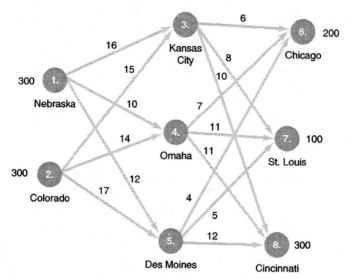

As with the transportation problem, a linear programming model is developed with supply and demand constraints. The supply constraints for the farms in Nebraska and Colorado are

$$x_{13} + x_{14} + x_{15} = 300$$
$$x_{23} + x_{24} + x_{25} = 300$$

The demand constraints at the Chicago, St. Louis, and Cincinnati mills are

$$x_{36} + x_{46} + x_{56} = 200$$
$$x_{37} + x_{47} + x_{57} = 100$$
$$x_{38} + x_{48} + x_{58} = 300$$

Next we must develop constraints for the grain elevators (i.e., transshipment points) at Kansas City, Omaha, and Des Moines. To develop these constraints we follow the principle that at each transshipment point the amount of grain shipped *in* must also be shipped *out*. For example the amount of grain shipped into Kansas City is

$$x_{13} + x_{23}$$

and the amount shipped out is

$$x_{36} + x_{37} + x_{38}$$

Thus, because whatever is shipped in must also be shipped out, these two amounts must equal each other

$$x_{13} + x_{23} = x_{36} + x_{37} + x_{38}$$

or

$$x_{13} + x_{23} - x_{36} - x_{37} - x_{38} = 0$$

The transshipment constraints for Omaha and Des Moines are constructed similarly.

$$x_{14} + x_{24} - x_{46} - x_{47} - x_{48} = 0$$
$$x_{15} + x_{25} - x_{56} - x_{57} - x_{58} = 0$$

The complete linear programming model, including the objective function, is summarized as follows.

$$\text{minimize } Z = \$16x_{13} + 10x_{14} + 12x_{15} + 15x_{23} + 14x_{24} + 17x_{25} + 6x_{36} + 8x_{37} + 10x_{38}$$
$$+ 7x_{46} + 11x_{47} + 11x_{48} + 4x_{56} + 5x_{57} + 12x_{58}$$

subject to

$$x_{13} + x_{14} + x_{15} = 300$$
$$x_{23} + x_{24} + x_{25} = 300$$
$$x_{36} + x_{46} + x_{56} = 200$$
$$x_{37} + x_{47} + x_{57} = 100$$
$$x_{38} + x_{48} + x_{58} = 300$$
$$x_{13} + x_{23} - x_{36} - x_{37} - x_{38} = 0$$
$$x_{14} + x_{24} - x_{46} - x_{47} - x_{48} = 0$$
$$x_{15} + x_{25} - x_{56} - x_{57} - x_{58} = 0$$
$$x_{ij} \geq 0$$

Computer Solution with Excel

Because the transshipment model is formulated as a linear programming model it can be solved with either Excel or QM for Windows. Here we will demonstrate its solution with Excel.

Exhibit 10 shows the spreadsheet solution and Exhibit 11 the solver for our wheat-shipping transshipment example. The spreadsheet is similar to the original spreadsheet for the regular transportation problem in Exhibit 1, except there are two tables of variables—one for shipping from the farms to the grain elevators and one for shipping grain from the elevators to the mills. Thus, the decision variables (i.e., the amounts shipped from sources to destinations) are in cells **B6:D7** and **C13:E15**. The constraint for the amount of grain shipped from the farm in Nebraska to the three grain elevators (i.e., the supply constraint for Nebraska) in cell F6 is "**=SUM(B6:D6)**," which sums cells "**B6+C6+D6**." The amount of

Exhibit 10

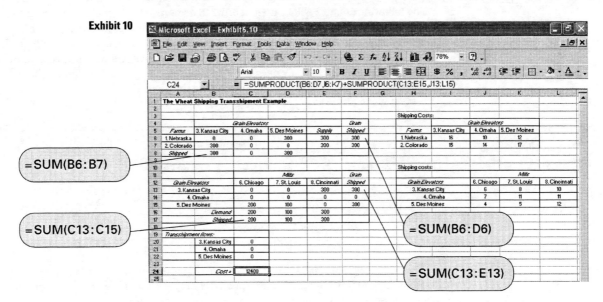

grain shipped to Kansas City from the farms in cell B8 is "**=SUM(B6:B7)**." Similar constraints are developed for the shipments from the grain elevators to the mills.

The objective function in Exhibit 10 is also constructed a bit differently than it was in Exhibit 1. Instead of typing in a single objective function in cell C24, two cost arrays have

Exhibit 11

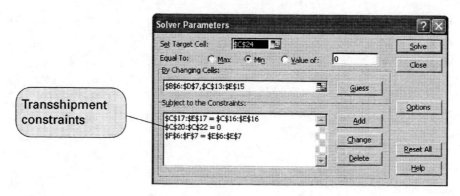

Transshipment constraints

been developed for the shipping costs in cells **I6:K7** and cells **J13:L15**, which are then multiplied times the variables in cells **B6:D7** and **C13:E15**, and added together. This objective function, "**=SUMPRODUCT(B6:D7,I6:K7)+SUMPRODUCT(C13:E15,J13:L15)**" is shown on the toolbar at the top of Exhibit 10. Constructing the objective function with cost arrays like this is a little easier than typing in all the variables and costs in a single objective function when there are a lot of variables and costs.

The Assignment Model

*An **assignment problem** is a special form of transportation problem in which all supply and demand values equal one.*

The assignment model is a special form of a linear programming model that is similar to the transportation model. There are differences, however. In the assignment model, the supply at each source and the demand at each destination are each limited to one unit.

The following example will be used in order to demonstrate the assignment model. The Atlantic Coast Conference (ACC) has four basketball games on a particular night. The conference office wants to assign four teams of officials to the four games in a way that will minimize the total distance traveled by the officials. The supply is always one team of officials, and the demand is for only one team of officials at each game. The distances in miles for each team of officials to each game location are shown in Table 1.

Table 1
The travel distances to each game for each team of officials

Officials	Game Sites			
	RALEIGH	ATLANTA	DURHAM	CLEMSON
A	210	90	180	160
B	100	70	130	200
C	175	105	140	170
D	80	65	105	120

The linear programming formulation of the assignment model is similar to the formulation of the transportation model, except all the supply values for each source equal one, and all the demand values at each destination equal one. Thus, our example is formulated as follows.

$$\text{minimize } Z = 210x_{AR} + 90x_{AA} + 180x_{AD} + 160x_{AC} + 100x_{BR} + 70x_{BA} + 130x_{BD}$$
$$+ 200x_{BC} + 175x_{CR} + 105x_{CA} + 140x_{CD} + 170x_{CC} + 80x_{DR} + 65x_{DA}$$
$$+ 105x_{DD} + 120x_{DC}$$

subject to

$$x_{AR} + x_{AA} + x_{AD} + x_{AC} = 1$$
$$x_{BR} + x_{BA} + x_{BD} + x_{BC} = 1$$
$$x_{CR} + x_{CA} + x_{CD} + x_{CC} = 1$$
$$x_{DR} + x_{DA} + x_{DD} + x_{DC} = 1$$
$$x_{AR} + x_{BR} + x_{CR} + x_{DR} = 1$$
$$x_{AA} + x_{BA} + x_{CA} + x_{DA} = 1$$
$$x_{AD} + x_{BD} + x_{CD} + x_{DD} = 1$$
$$x_{AC} + x_{BC} + x_{CC} + x_{DC} = 1$$
$$x_{ij} \geq 0$$

This is a *balanced* assignment model. An *unbalanced* model exists when supply exceeds demand or demand exceeds supply.

Computer Solution of the Assignment Problem

The assignment problem can be solved using the assignment module in QM for Windows and with Excel spreadsheets. We will solve our example of assigning ACC officials to game sites first using Excel and then QM for Windows.

Computer Solution with Excel

As was the case with transportation problems, Excel can be used to solve assignment problems but only as linear programming models. Exhibit 12 shows an Excel spreadsheet for our ACC basketball officials example. The objective function in cell C11 was developed by creating a cost array in cells **C16:F19** and multiplying it by the decision variables in cells **C5:F8**. The model constraints for available teams (supply) are contained in the cells in column H, and the constraints, for officials teams at the game sites (demand) are contained in the cells in row 10.

Exhibit 12

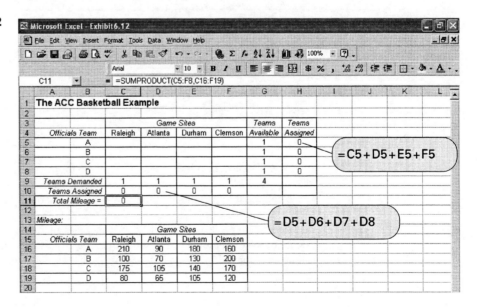

Exhibit 13 shows the "Solver Parameters" screen for our example. Before clicking on "Solve," remember to invoke the "Options" screen and click on "Assume Linear Model" to solve as a linear programming model. The optimal solution is shown in Exhibit 14.

Exhibit 13

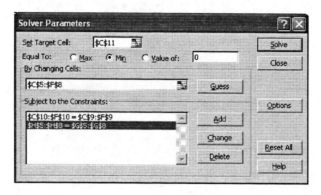

Exhibit 14

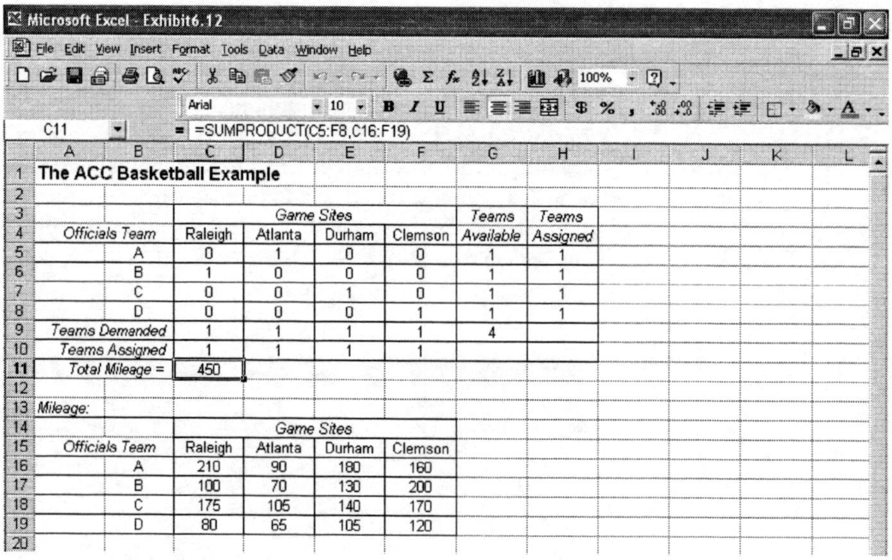

		Game Sites				Teams	Teams
Officials Team		Raleigh	Atlanta	Durham	Clemson	Available	Assigned
A		0	1	0	0	1	1
B		1	0	0	0	1	1
C		0	0	1	0	1	1
D		0	0	0	1	1	1
Teams Demanded		1	1	1	1	4	
Teams Assigned		1	1	1	1		
Total Mileage =		450					

Mileage:

		Game Sites			
Officials Team		Raleigh	Atlanta	Durham	Clemson
A		210	90	180	160
B		100	70	130	200
C		175	105	140	170
D		80	65	105	120

The ACC Basketball Example

C11 = =SUMPRODUCT(C5:F8,C16:F19)

Excel QM also includes a spreadsheet macro for the assignment problem. It is very similar to the Excel QM macro we demonstrated earlier in this chapter for the transportation problem and the spreadsheet setup is very much like the Excel spreadsheet in Exhibit 14. The assignment macro is accessed (from the "QM" menu) and applied similarly to the transportation problem macro. It already includes all the cell and constraint formulas necessary to solve the problem. The solution to our ACC basketball example with Excel QM is shown in Exhibit 15.

Exhibit 15

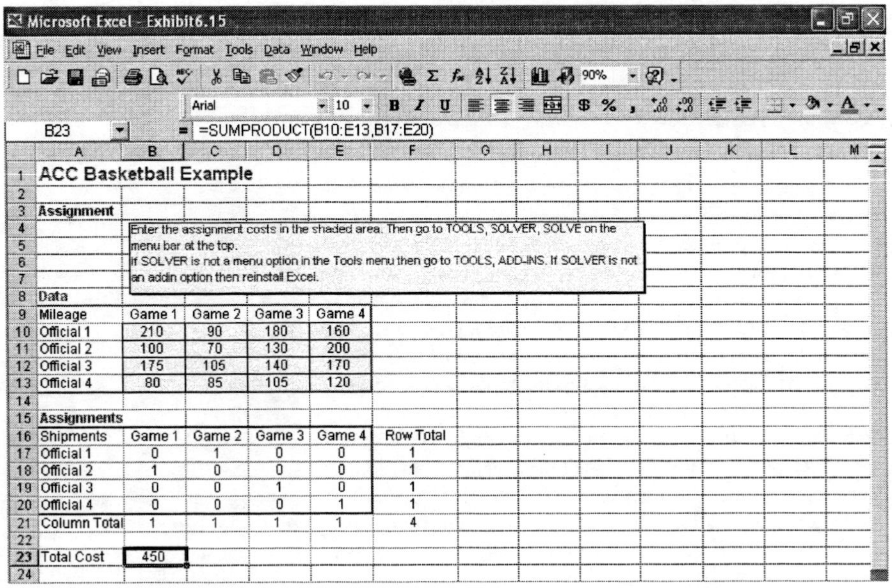

Microsoft Excel - Exhibit6.15													

B23 = =SUMPRODUCT(B10:E13,B17:E20)

	A	B	C	D	E	F	G	H	I	J	K	L	M
1	ACC Basketball Example												
2													
3	Assignment												
4		Enter the assignment costs in the shaded area. Then go to TOOLS, SOLVER, SOLVE on the											
5		menu bar at the top.											
6		If SOLVER is not a menu option in the Tools menu then go to TOOLS, ADD-INS. If SOLVER is not											
7		an addin option then reinstall Excel.											
8	Data												
9	Mileage	Game 1	Game 2	Game 3	Game 4								
10	Official 1	210	90	180	160								
11	Official 2	100	70	130	200								
12	Official 3	175	105	140	170								
13	Official 4	80	85	105	120								
14													
15	Assignments												
16	Shipments	Game 1	Game 2	Game 3	Game 4	Row Total							
17	Official 1	0	1	0	0	1							
18	Official 2	1	0	0	0	1							
19	Official 3	0	0	1	0	1							
20	Official 4	0	0	0	1	1							
21	Column Total	1	1	1	1	4							
22													
23	Total Cost	450											
24													

**Computer Solution
with QM for Windows**

The data input for our example is shown in Exhibit 16 followed by the solution in Exhibit 17.

Exhibit 16

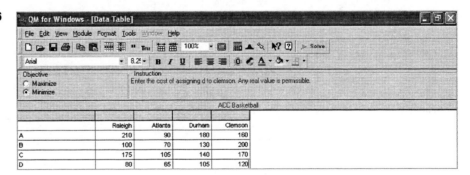

QM for Windows - [Data Table]

File Edit View Module Format Tools Window Help

Objective
○ Maximize
● Minimize

Instruction
Enter the cost of assigning d to clemson. Any real value is permissible.

ACC Basketball

	Raleigh	Atlanta	Durham	Clemson
A	210	90	180	160
B	100	70	130	200
C	175	105	140	170
D	80	65	105	120

Exhibit 17

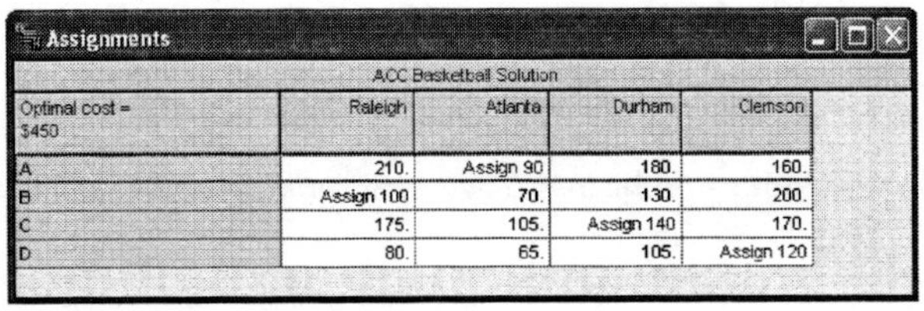

Assignments

ACC Basketball Solution

Optimal cost = $450	Raleigh	Atlanta	Durham	Clemson
A	210.	Assign 90	180.	160.
B	Assign 100	70.	130.	200.
C	175.	105.	Assign 140	170.
D	80.	65.	105.	Assign 120

Management Science Application

Assigning Managers to Construction Projects

The Nashville office of Heery International contracts with the state of Tennessee, various municipalities, and private firms for construction projects such as hospitals, office buildings, state park facilities, university libraries, dorms and classroom buildings, and prisons. Projects average about $2 million although they can vary in size from $50,000 up to $50 million. When assigning managers to projects, Heery's objective is to minimize the total cost while maintaining a balanced workload among its managers. At any one time, Heery will have approximately 7 managers (who live in different cities) that it must assign to up to 114 projects. Heery developed a modified version of the assignment model that is solved using an Excel spreadsheet. The solution approach is robust enough to handle new projects, the termination of old projects, the resignation of managers, and the hiring of new managers over the passage of time.

The objective function in Heery's model is to minimize project intensity (instead of cost). Project intensity is a logarithmic function of project cost and manager driving time to a project. This intensity function quantifies a manager's effort by assigning relative (dimensionless) values to the projects based on a project's dollar value and the time required for the manager to drive to a project. As projects get larger (in dollar value) there is less difference between the intensities necessary to manage them. The model includes constraints that balance the monthly workload given to each manager. One set of constraints limits each manager's total intensity to a maximum amount each month for the next 12 months. Another set of constraints ensures fairness by specifying that each manager's total monthly intensity must be at least a specified amount. A final set of constraints ensures that each project must have exactly one manager assigned to it. In some cases experienced managers are assigned to more important projects a priori manually in the spreadsheet. Also, continuity of previous assignments to ongoing projects is necessary. Further,

Photo courtesy of AP/Wide World Photos

some projects in an outlying area might require the same manager simply because of their proximity to each other. For example, three projects at Middle Tennessee State University—stadium, bookstore, and library—needed to be managed by one person.

Because of the natural progression of construction projects over time, Heery updates the spreadsheet model each month at its Nashville office. The assignment model has saved Heery money by enabling it to reduce its number of managers, reduce travel costs for managers, and reduce the time required to prepare project assignments each month. It has also improved morale because workloads are perceived to be fairer.

Source: L. J. LeBlanc, D. Randels, Jr., and T. K. Swann, "Heery International's Spreadsheet Optimization Model for Assigning Managers to Construction Projects," *Interfaces* 30, no. 6 (November–December 2000): 95–106.

Summary

In this chapter three special types of linear programming problems were presented—the transportation problem, the transshipment problem, and the assignment problem. As we mentioned at the beginning of the chapter, they are part of a larger class of linear programming problems known as network flow problems.

References

Ackoff, R. L., and Sasieni, M. W. *Fundamentals of Operations Research*. New York: John Wiley & Sons, 1968.

Charnes, A., and Cooper, W. W. *Management Models and Industrial Applications of Linear Programming*. New York: John Wiley & Sons, 1961.

Churchman, C. W., Ackoff, R. L., and Arnoff, E. L. *Introduction to Operations Research*. New York: John Wiley & Sons, 1957.

Hitchcock, F. L. "The Distribution of a Product from Several Sources to Numerous Localities." *Journal of Mathematics and Physics* 20 (1941): 224, 230.

Koopmans, T. C., ed. *Activity Analysis of Production and Allocation*. Cowles Commission Monograph No. 13. New York: John Wiley & Sons, 1951.

Orchard-Hays, W. *Advanced Linear Programming Computing Techniques*. New York: McGraw-Hill, 1968.

Taha, H. A. *Operations Research*. 4th ed. New York: Macmillan, 1987.

Example Problem Solution

This example will demonstrate the procedure for solving a transportation problem.

Problem Statement

A concrete company transports concrete from three plants to three construction sites. The supply capacities of the three plants, the demand requirements at the three sites, and the transportation costs per ton are as follows.

Plant	Construction Site			Supply (tons)
	A	*B*	*C*	
1	$ 8	$ 5	$ 6	120
2	15	10	12	80
3	3	9	10	80
Demand (tons)	150	70	100	280

Determine the linear programming model formulation for this problem and solve using Excel.

Solution

Step 1: The Linear Programming Model Formulation

minimize $Z = \$8x_{1A} + 5x_{1B} + 6x_{1C} + 15x_{2A} + 10x_{2B} + 12x_{2C} + 3x_{3A} + 9x_{3B} + 10x_{3C}$

subject to

$$x_{1A} + x_{1B} + x_{1C} = 120$$
$$x_{2A} + x_{2B} + x_{2C} = 80$$
$$x_{3A} + x_{3B} + x_{3C} = 80$$
$$x_{1A} + x_{2A} + x_{3A} \leq 150$$
$$x_{1B} + x_{2B} + x_{3B} \leq 70$$
$$x_{1C} + x_{2C} + x_{3C} \leq 100$$
$$x_{ij} \geq 0$$

Step 2: Excel Solution

Problems

1. Green Valley Mills produces carpet at plants in St. Louis and Richmond. The carpet is then shipped to two outlets located in Chicago and Atlanta. The cost per ton of shipping carpet from each of the two plants to the two warehouses is as follows.

	To	
From	Chicago	Atlanta
St. Louis	$40	$65
Richmond	70	30

The plant at St. Louis can supply 250 tons of carpet per week; the plant at Richmond can supply 400 tons per week. The Chicago outlet has a demand of 300 tons per week, and the outlet at Atlanta demands 350 tons per week. The company wants to know the number of tons of carpet to ship from each plant to each outlet in order to minimize the total shipping cost. Solve this transportation problem.

2. A transportation problem involves the following costs, supply, and demand.

	To				
From	1	2	3	4	Supply
1	$500	$750	$300	$450	12
2	650	800	400	600	17
3	400	700	500	550	11
Demand	10	10	10	10	

Solve this problem using the computer.

3. Given a transportation problem with the following costs, supply, and demand, find the optimal solution using the computer.

From	To 1	2	3	Supply
A	$6	$7	$4	100
B	5	3	6	180
C	8	5	7	200
Demand	135	175	170	

4. Consider the following transportation problem.

From	To 1	2	3	Supply
A	$ 6	$9	$M	130
B	12	3	5	70
C	4	8	11	100
Demand	80	110	60	

Formulate this problem as a linear programming model and solve using the computer.

5. Solve the following linear programming problem.

$$\text{minimize } Z = 3x_{11} + 12x_{12} + 8x_{13} + 10x_{21} + 5x_{22} + 6x_{23} + 6x_{31} + 7x_{32} + 10x_{33}$$

subject to

$$x_{11} + x_{12} + x_{13} = 90$$
$$x_{21} + x_{22} + x_{23} = 30$$
$$x_{31} + x_{32} + x_{33} = 100$$
$$x_{11} + x_{21} + x_{31} \leq 70$$
$$x_{12} + x_{22} + x_{32} \leq 110$$
$$x_{13} + x_{23} + x_{33} \leq 80$$
$$x_{ij} \geq 0$$

6. Consider the following transportation problem.

From	To 1	2	3	Supply
A	$6	$9	$ 7	130
B	12	3	5	70
C	4	8	11	100
Demand	80	110	60	

Solve using the computer.

7. Steel mills in three cities produce the following amounts of steel.

Location	Weekly Production (tons)
A. Bethlehem	150
B. Birmingham	210
C. Gary	320
	680

These mills supply steel to four cities where manufacturing plants have the following demand.

Location	Weekly Demand (tons)
1. Detroit	130
2. St. Louis	70
3. Chicago	180
4. Norfolk	240
	620

Shipping costs per ton of steel are as follows.

From	To			
	1	2	3	4
A	$14	$ 9	$16	$18
B	11	8	7	16
C	16	12	10	22

Because of a truckers' strike, shipments are prohibited from Birmingham to Chicago. Formulate this problem as a linear programming model and solve using the computer.

8. In problem 7, what would be the effect on the optimal solution of a reduction in production capacity at the Gary mill from 320 tons to 290 tons per week?

9. Coal is mined and processed at the following four mines in Kentucky, West Virginia, and Virginia.

Location	Capacity (tons)
A. Cabin Creek	90
B. Surry	50
C. Old Fort	80
D. McCoy	60
	280

These mines supply the following amount of coal to utility power plants in three cities.

Plant	Demand (tons)
1. Richmond	120
2. Winston-Salem	100
3. Durham	110
	330

The railroad shipping costs ($1,000s) per ton of coal are shown in the following table. Because of railroad construction, shipments are prohibited from Cabin Creek to Richmond.

	To		
From	1	2	3
A	$7	10	5
B	12	9	4
C	7	3	11
D	9	5	7

Formulate this problem as a linear programming model and solve using the computer.

10. Oranges are grown, picked, and then stored in warehouses in Tampa, Miami, and Fresno. These warehouses supply oranges to markets in New York, Philadelphia, Chicago, and Boston. The following table shows the shipping costs per truckload ($100s), supply, and demand. Because of an agreement between distributors, shipments are prohibited from Miami to Chicago.

	To				
From	New York	Philadelphia	Chicago	Boston	Supply
Tampa	$ 9	$ 14	$ 12	$ 17	200
Miami	11	10	6	10	200
Fresno	12	8	15	7	200
Demand	130	170	100	150	

Formulate this problem as a linear programming model, and solve using the computer.

11. A manufacturing firm produces diesel engines in four cities—Phoenix, Seattle, St. Louis, and Detroit. The company is able to produce the following numbers of engines per month.

Plant	Production
1. Phoenix	5
2. Seattle	25
3. St. Louis	20
4. Detroit	25

Three trucking firms purchase the following numbers of engines for their plants in three cities.

Firm	Demand
A. Greensboro	10
B. Charlotte	20
C. Louisville	15

The transportation costs per engine ($100s) from sources to destinations are shown in the following table. However, the Charlotte firm will not accept engines made in Seattle, and the Louisville firm will not accept engines from Detroit; therefore, these routes are prohibited.

From	To		
	A	B	C
1	$7	$8	$5
2	6	10	6
3	10	4	5
4	3	9	11

Formulate this problem as a linear programming model and solve using the computer.

12. The Interstate Truck Rental firm has accumulated extra trucks at three of its truck leasing outlets, as shown in the following table.

Leasing Outlet	Extra Trucks
1. Atlanta	70
2. St. Louis	115
3. Greensboro	60
Total	245

The firm also has four outlets with shortages of rental trucks, as follows.

Leasing Outlet	Truck Shortage
A. New Orleans	80
B. Cincinnati	50
C. Louisville	90
D. Pittsburgh	25
Total	245

The firm wants to transfer trucks from those outlets with extras to those with shortages at the minimum total cost. The following costs of transporting these trucks from city to city have been determined.

From	To			
	A	B	C	D
1	$70	$80	$45	$90
2	120	40	30	75
3	110	60	70	80

Solve this problem using the computer.

13. The Shotz Beer Company has breweries in two cities; the breweries can supply the following numbers of barrels of draft beer to the company's distributors each month.

Brewery	Monthly Supply (bbl)
A. Tampa	3,500
B. St. Louis	5,000
Total	8,500

The distributors, which are spread throughout six states, have the following total monthly demand.

Distributor	Monthly Demand (bbl)
1. Tennessee	1,600
2. Georgia	1,800
3. North Carolina	1,500
4. South Carolina	950
5. Kentucky	1,250
6. Virginia	1,400
Total	8,500

The company must pay the following shipping costs per barrel.

	To					
From	1	2	3	4	5	6
A	$0.50	$0.35	$0.60	$0.45	$0.80	$0.75
B	0.25	0.65	0.40	0.55	0.20	0.65

Solve this problem using the computer.

14. In problem 13, the Shotz Beer Company management has negotiated a new shipping contract with a trucking firm between its Tampa brewery and its distributor in Kentucky. This contract reduces the shipping cost per barrel from $0.80 per barrel to $0.65 per barrel. How will this cost change affect the optimal solution?

15. Computers Unlimited sells microcomputers to universities and colleges on the East Coast and ships them from three distribution warehouses. The firm is able to supply the following numbers of microcomputers to the universities by the beginning of the academic year.

Distribution Warehouse	Supply (microcomputers)
1. Richmond	420
2. Atlanta	610
3. Washington, D.C.	340
Total	1,370

Four universities have ordered microcomputers that must be delivered and installed by the beginning of the academic year.

University	Demand (microcomputers)
A. Tech	520
B. A and M	250
C. State	400
D. Central	380
Total	1,550

The shipping and installation costs per microcomputer from each distributor to each university are as follows.

	To			
From	A	B	C	D
1	$22	$17	$30	$18
2	15	35	20	25
3	28	21	16	14

Solve this problem using the computer.

16. In problem 15, Computers Unlimited wants to better meet demand at the four universities it supplies. It is considering two alternatives: (1) expand its warehouse at Richmond to a capacity of 600 at a cost equivalent to an additional $6 in handling and shipping per unit; or (2) purchase a new warehouse in Charlotte that can supply 300 units with shipping costs of $19 to Tech, $26 to A and M, $22 to State, and $16 to Central. Which alternative should management select based solely on transportation costs (i.e., no capital costs)?

17. Computers Unlimited in problem 15 has determined that when it is unable to meet the demand for microcomputers at the universities it supplies, the universities tend to purchase microcomputers elsewhere in the future. Thus, the firm has estimated a shortage cost for each microcomputer demanded but not supplied that reflects the loss of future sales and goodwill. These costs for each university are as follows.

University	Cost/Microcomputer
A. Tech	$40
B. A and M	65
C. State	25
D. Central	50

Solve problem 15 with these shortage costs included. Compute the total transportation cost and the total shortage cost.

18. A severe winter ice storm has swept across North Carolina and Virginia, followed by over a foot of snow and frigid, single-digit temperatures. These weather conditions have resulted in numerous downed power lines and power outages, causing dangerous conditions for much of the population. Local utility companies have been overwhelmed and have requested assistance from unaffected utility companies across the Southeast. The following table shows the number of utility trucks with crews available from five different companies in Georgia, South Carolina, and Florida; the demand for crews in seven different areas that local companies cannot get to; and the weekly cost ($1,000s) of a crew going to a specific area (based on the visiting company's normal charges, the distance the crew has to come, and living expenses in an area).

| Crew | Area (Cost = $1,000s) | | | | | | | Crews Available |
	NC-E	NC-SW	NC-P	NC-W	VA-SW	VA-C	VA-T	
GA-1	15.2	14.3	13.9	13.5	14.7	16.5	18.7	12
GA-2	12.8	11.3	10.6	12.0	12.7	13.2	15.6	10
SC-1	12.4	10.8	9.4	11.3	13.1	12.8	14.5	14
FL-1	18.2	19.4	18.2	17.9	20.5	20.7	22.7	15
FL-2	19.3	20.2	19.5	20.2	21.2	21.3	23.5	12
Crews Needed	9	7	6	8	10	9	7	

Determine the number of crews that should be sent from each utility to each affected area that will minimize total costs.

19. A large manufacturing company is closing three of its existing plants and intends to transfer some of its more skilled employees to three plants that will remain open. The number of employees available for transfer from each closing plant is as follows.

Closing Plant	Transferable Employees
1	60
2	105
3	70
Total	235

The following number of employees can be accommodated at the three plants remaining open.

Open Plants	Employees Demanded
A	45
B	90
C	35
Total	170

Each transferred employee will increase product output per day at each plant as shown in the following table. The company wants to transfer employees to ensure the maximum increase in product output.

	To		
From	A	B	C
1	5	8	6
2	10	9	12
3	7	6	8

Solve this problem using the computer.

20. The Sav-Us Rental Car Agency has six lots in Nashville, and it wants to have a certain number of cars available at each lot at the beginning of each day for local rental. The agency would like a model it could quickly solve at the end of each day that would tell it how to redistribute the cars among the six lots in the minimum total time. The time required to travel between the six lots are as follows.

	To (minutes)					
From	1	2	3	4	5	6
1	—	12	17	18	10	20
2	14	—	10	19	16	15
3	14	10	—	12	8	9
4	8	16	14	—	12	15
5	11	21	16	18	—	10
6	24	12	9	17	15	—

The agency would like the following number of cars at each lot at the end of the day. Also shown is the number of available cars at each lot at the end of a particular day. Determine the optimal reallocation of rental cars using any initial solution approach and any solution method.

	Lot					
Cars	1	2	3	4	5	6
Available	37	20	14	26	40	28
Desired	30	25	20	40	30	20

21. Bayville has built a new elementary school, increasing the town's total to four schools—Addison, Beeks, Canfield, and Daley. Each has a capacity of 400 students. The school board wants to assign children to schools so that their travel time by bus is as short as possible. The school board has par-

titioned the town into five districts conforming to population density—north, south, east, west, and central. The average bus travel time from each district to each school is shown as follows.

District	Travel Time (mins)				Student Population
	Addison	Beeks	Canfield	Daley	
North	12	23	35	17	250
South	26	15	21	27	340
East	18	20	22	31	310
West	29	24	35	10	210
Central	15	10	23	16	290

Determine the number of children that should be assigned from each district to each school to minimize total student travel time.

22. In problem 21, the school board has determined that it does not want any of the schools to be overly crowded compared with the other schools. It would like to assign students from each district to each school so that enrollments are evenly balanced between the four schools. However, the school board is concerned that this might significantly increase travel time. Determine the number of students to be assigned from each district to each school such that school enrollments are evenly balanced. Does this new solution appear to significantly increase travel time per student?

23. The Easy Time Grocery chain operates in major metropolitan areas on the eastern seaboard. The stores have a "no-frills" approach, with low overhead and high volume. They generally buy their stock in volume at low prices. However, in some cases they actually buy stock at stores in other areas and ship it in. They can do this because of high prices in the cities they operate in compared with costs in other locations. One example is baby food. Easy Time purchases baby food at stores in Albany, Binghamton, Claremont, Dover, and Edison, and then trucks it to six stores in and around New York City. The stores in the outlying areas know what Easy Time is up to, so they limit the number of cases of baby food Easy Time can purchase. The following table shows the profit Easy Time makes per case of baby food based on where the chain purchases it and at which store it is sold, plus the available baby food per week at purchase locations and the shelf space available at each Easy Time store per week.

Purchase Location	Easy Time Store						Supply
	1	2	3	4	5	6	
Albany	9	8	11	12	7	8	26
Binghamton	10	10	8	6	9	7	40
Claremont	8	6	6	5	7	4	20
Dover	4	6	9	5	8	10	40
Edison	12	10	8	9	6	7	45
Demand	25	15	30	18	27	35	

Determine where Easy Time should purchase baby food and how the food should be distributed to maximize profit.

24. Suppose that in problem 23 Easy Time can purchase all the baby food it needs from a New York City distributor at a price that will result in a profit of $9 per case at stores 1, 3, and 4, $8 per case at stores 2 and 6, and $7 per case at store 5. Should Easy Time purchase all, none, or some of its baby food from the distributor rather than purchasing it at other stores and trucking it in?

25. In problem 23, if Easy Time could arrange to purchase more baby food from one of the outlying locations, which should it be, how many additional cases could be purchased, and how much would this increase profit?

26. The Roadnet Transport Company has expanded its shipping capacity by purchasing 90 trailer trucks from a competitor that went bankrupt. The company subsequently located 30 of the purchased trucks at each of its shipping warehouses in Charlotte, Memphis, and Louisville. The company makes shipments from each of these warehouses to terminals in St. Louis, Atlanta, and New York. Each truck is capable of making one shipment per week. The terminal managers have indicated their capacity of extra shipments. The manager at St. Louis can accommodate 40 additional trucks per week, the manager at Atlanta can accommodate 60 additional trucks, and the manager at New York can accommodate 50 additional trucks. The company makes the following profit per truckload shipment from each warehouse to each terminal. The profits differ as a result of differences in products shipped, shipping costs, and transport rates.

Warehouse	Terminal		
	St. Louis	Atlanta	New York
Charlotte	$1,800	$2,100	$1,600
Memphis	1,000	700	900
Louisville	1,400	800	2,200

Determine how many trucks to assign to each route (i.e., warehouse to terminal) in order to maximize profit.

27. During the war in Iraq, large amounts of military matériel and supplies had to be shipped daily from supply depots in the United States to bases in the Middle East. The critical factor in the movement of these supplies was speed. The following table shows the number of planeloads of supplies available each day from each of six supply depots and the number of daily loads demanded at each of five bases. (Each planeload is approximately equal in tonnage.) Also included are the transport hours per plane, including loading and fueling, actual flight time, and unloading and refueling.

Supply Depot	Military Base					Supply
	A	B	C	D	E	
1	36	40	32	43	29	7
2	28	27	29	40	38	10
3	34	35	41	29	31	8
4	41	42	35	27	36	8
5	25	28	40	34	38	9
6	31	30	43	38	40	6
Demand	9	6	12	8	10	

Determine the optimal daily flight schedule that will minimize total transport time.

28. PM Computer Services produces personal computers from component parts it buys on the open market. The company can produce a maximum of 300 personal computers per month. PM wants to determine its production schedule for the first six months of the new year. The cost to produce a personal computer in January will be $1,200. However, PM knows the cost of component parts will decline each month so that the overall cost to produce a PC will be 5% less each month. The cost of holding a computer in inventory is $15 per unit per month. Following is the demand for the company's computers each month.

Month	Demand	Month	Demand
January	180	April	210
February	260	May	400
March	340	June	320

Determine a production schedule for PM that will minimize total cost.

29. In problem 28, suppose the demand for personal computers increased each month as follows.

Month	Demand
January	410
February	320
March	500
April	620
May	430
June	380

In addition to the regular production capacity of 300 units per month, PM Computer Services can also produce an additional 200 computers per month using overtime. Overtime production adds 20% to the cost of a personal computer.

Determine a production schedule for PM that will minimize total cost.

30. National Foods Company has five plants where it processes and packages fruits and vegetables. It has suppliers in six cities in California, Texas, Alabama, and Florida. The company has owned and operated its own trucking system in the past for transporting fruits and vegetables from its suppliers to its plants. However, it is now considering outsourcing all of its shipping to outside trucking firms and getting rid of its own trucks. It currently spends $245,000 per month to operate its own trucking system. It has determined monthly shipping costs (in $1,000s per ton) using outside shippers from each of its suppliers to each of its plants as shown in the following table.

Suppliers	Processing Plants ($1,000s/ton)					Supply (tons)
	Denver	St. Paul	Louisville	Akron	Topeka	
Sacramento	3.7	4.6	4.9	5.5	4.3	18
Bakersfield	3.4	5.1	4.4	5.9	5.2	15
San Antonio	3.3	4.1	3.7	2.9	2.6	10
Montgomery	1.9	4.2	2.7	5.4	3.9	12
Jacksonville	6.1	5.1	3.8	2.5	4.1	20
Ocala	6.6	4.8	3.5	3.6	4.5	15
Demand (tons)	20	15	15	15	20	90

Should National Foods continue to operate its own shipping network or sell its trucks and outsource its shipping to independent trucking firms?

31. In problem 30, National Foods would like to know what the effect would be on the optimal solution and the company's decision regarding its shipping if it negotiates with its suppliers in Sacramento, Jacksonville, and Ocala to increase their capacity to 25 tons per month. What would be the effect of negotiating instead with its suppliers at San Antonio and Montgomery to increase their capacity to 25 tons each?

32. Orient Express is a global distribution company that transports its clients' products to customers in Hong Kong, Singapore, and Taipei. All of the products Orient Express ships are stored at three distribution centers—one in Los Angeles, one in Savannah, and one in Galveston. For the coming month the company has 450 containers of computer components available at the Los Angeles center, 600 containers available at Savannah, and 350 containers available in Galveston. The company has orders for 600 containers from Hong Kong, 500 containers from Singapore, and 500 containers from Taipei. The shipping costs per container from each U.S. port to each of the overseas ports are shown in the following table.

U.S. Distribution Center	Overseas Port		
	Hong Kong	Singapore	Taipei
Los Angeles	$300	$210	$340
Savannah	490	520	610
Galveston	360	320	500

The Orient Express as the overseas broker for its U.S. customers is responsible for unfulfilled orders, and it incurs stiff penalty costs from overseas customers if it does not meet an order. The Hong Kong customers charge a penalty cost of $800 per container for unfulfilled demand, Singapore customers charge a penalty cost of $920 per container, and Taipei customers charge $1,100 per container. Formulate and solve a transportation model to determine the shipments from each U.S. distribution center to each overseas port that will minimize shipping costs. Indicate what portion of the total cost is a result of penalties.

33. Binford Tools manufactures garden tools. It uses inventory, overtime, and subcontracting to absorb demand fluctuations. Expected demand, regular and overtime production capacity, and subcontracting capacity are provided in the following table for the next four quarters for its basic line of steel garden tools.

Quarter	Demand	Regular Capacity	Overtime Capacity	Subcontracting Capacity
1	9,000	9,000	1,000	3,000
2	12,000	10,000	1,500	3,000
3	16,000	12,000	2,000	3,000
4	19,000	12,000	2,000	3,000

The regular production cost per unit is $20, the overtime cost per unit is $25, the cost to subcontract a unit is $27, and the inventory carrying cost is $2 per unit. The company has 300 units in inventory at the beginning of the year.

Determine the optimal production schedule for the four quarters that will minimize total costs.

34. Al, Barbara, Carol, and Dave have joined together to purchase two season tickets to the Giants' home football games. Because there are eight home games, each person will get tickets to two games. Each person has ranked the games they prefer from 1 to 8, with 1 being most preferred and 8 least preferred, as follows.

| Game | Person | | | |
	Al	Barbara	Carol	Dave
1. Cowboys	1	2	1	4
2. Redskins	3	4	4	1
3. Cardinals	7	8	8	7
4. Eagles	2	7	5	3
5. Bengals	5	6	6	8
6. Packers	6	3	2	5
7. Saints	8	5	7	6
8. Jets	4	1	3	2

Determine the two games each person should get tickets for that will result in the groups' greatest degree of satisfaction. Do you think the participants would think your allocation is fair?

35. World Foods, Inc., imports food products such as meats, cheeses, and pastries to the United States from warehouses at ports in Hamburg, Marseilles, and Liverpool. Ships from these ports deliver the products to Norfolk, New York, and Savannah, where they are stored in company warehouses before being shipped to distribution centers in Dallas, St. Louis, and Chicago. The products are then distributed to specialty food stores and sold through catalogs. The shipping costs ($/1,000 lb) from the European ports to the U.S. cities and the available supply (1,000 lb) at the European ports are provided in the following table.

| European Port | U.S. Cities | | | Supply |
	4. Norfolk	5. New York	6. Savannah	
1. Hamburg	$420	$390	$610	55
2. Marseilles	510	590	470	78
3. Liverpool	450	360	480	37

The transportation costs ($/1,000 lb) from each U.S. city of the three distribution centers and the demand (1,000 lb) at the distribution centers are as follows.

| Warehouse | Distribution Center | | |
	7. Dallas	8. St. Louis	9. Chicago
4. Norfolk	$ 75	$ 63	$81
5. New York	125	110	95
6. Savannah	68	82	95
	60	45	50

Determine the optimal shipments between the European ports and the warehouses and the distribution centers that will minimize total transportation costs.

36. A sports apparel company has received an order for a college basketball team's national championship T-shirt. The company can purchase the T-shirts from textile factories in Mexico, Puerto Rico, and Haiti. The shirts are shipped from the factories to companies in the United States that silk-screen the shirts before they are shipped to distribution centers. Following are the production and transportation costs ($/shirt) from the T-shirt factories to the silk-screen companies to the distribution centers, plus the supply of T-shirts at the factories and demand for the shirts at the distribution centers.

| | Silk-screen Companies | | | |
T-shirt Factory	4. Miami	5. Atlanta	6. Houston	Supply (1,000s)
1. Mexico	$4	$6	$3	18
2. Puerto Rico	3	5	5	15
3. Haiti	2	4	4	23

| | Distribution Centers | | |
Silk-screen Company	7. New York	8. St. Louis	9. Los Angeles
4. Miami	$ 5	$ 7	$ 9
5. Atlanta	7	6	10
6. Houston	8	6	8
Demand (1,000s)	20	12	20

Determine the optimal shipments that will minimize total production and transportation costs for the apparel company.

37. Walsh's Fruit Company contracts with growers in Ohio, Pennsylvania, and New York to purchase grapes. The grapes are processed into juice at the farms and stored in refrigerated vats. Then the juice is shipped to two plants, where it is processed into bottled grape juice and frozen concentrate. The juice and concentrate are then transported to three food warehouses/distribution centers. The transportation costs per ton from the farms to the plants and from the plants to the distributors, and the supply at the farms and demand at the distribution centers are summarized in the following tables.

| | Plant | | |
Farm	4. Indiana	5. Georgia	Supply (1,000 tons)
1. Ohio	$16	21	72
2. Pennsylvania	18	16	105
3. New York	22	25	83

| | Distribution Centers | | |
Plant	6. Virginia	7. Kentucky	8. Louisiana
4. Indiana	$23	$15	$29
5. Georgia	20	17	24
Demand (1,000 tons)	90	80	120

a. Determine the optimal shipments from farms to plants to distribution centers that will minimize total transportation costs.

b. What would be the effect on the solution if the capacity at each plant was 140,000 tons?

38. A national catalog and Internet retailer has three warehouses and three major distribution centers located around the country. Normally, items are shipped directly from the warehouses to the distribution centers; however, each of the distribution centers can also be used as an intermediate transshipment point. The transportation costs ($/unit) between warehouses and distribution centers, the supply at the warehouses (100 units), and the demand at the distribution centers (100 units) for a specific week are shown in the following table.

	Distribution Center			
Warehouse	A	B	C	Supply
1	$12	$11	$ 7	70
2	8	6	14	80
3	9	10	12	50
Demand	60	100	40	

The transportation costs ($/unit) between the distribution centers are

	Distribution Center		
Distribution Center	A	B	C
A	—	8	3
B	1	—	2
C	7	2	—

Determine the optimal shipments between warehouses and distribution centers that will minimize total transportation costs.

39. Horizon Computers manufactures laptops in Germany, Belgium, and Italy. Because of high tariffs between international trade groups, it is sometimes cheaper to ship partially completed laptops to factories in Puerto Rico, Mexico, and Panama and have them completed before final shipment to U.S. distributors in Texas, Virginia, and Ohio. The cost ($/unit) of the completed laptops plus tariffs and shipment costs from the European plants directly to the United States and supply and demand are shown as follows.

	U.S. Distributors			
European Plants	7. Texas	8. Virginia	9. Ohio	Supply (1,000s)
1. Germany	$2,600	$1,900	$2,300	5.2
2. Belgium	2,200	2,100	2,600	6.3
3. Italy	1,800	2,200	2,500	4.5
Demand (1,000s)	2.1	3.7	7.8	

Alternatively, the unit costs of shipping partially completed laptops to plants for finishing before sending them to the United States are as follows.

European Plants	Factories		
	4. Puerto Rico	5. Mexico	6. Panama
1. Germany	$1,400	$1,200	$1,100
2. Belgium	1,600	1,100	900
3. Italy	1,500	1,400	1,200

Factories	U.S. Distributors		
	7. Texas	8. Virginia	9. Ohio
4. Puerto Rico	$800	$700	$ 900
5. Mexico	600	800	1,100
6. Panama	900	700	1,200

Determine the optimal shipments of laptops that will meet demand at the U.S. distributors at the minimum total cost.

40. Solve the following linear programming problem.

$$\text{minimize } Z = 18x_{11} + 30x_{12} + 20x_{13} + 18x_{14} + 25x_{21} + 27x_{22} + 22x_{23}$$
$$+ 16x_{24} + 30x_{31} + 26x_{32} + 19x_{33} + 32x_{34} + 40x_{41} + 36x_{42}$$
$$+ 27x_{43} + 29x_{44} + 30x_{51} + 26x_{52} + 18x_{53} + 24x_{54}$$

subject to

$$x_{11} + x_{12} + x_{13} + x_{14} \le 1$$
$$x_{21} + x_{22} + x_{23} + x_{24} \le 1$$
$$x_{31} + x_{32} + x_{33} + x_{34} \le 1$$
$$x_{41} + x_{42} + x_{43} + x_{44} \le 1$$
$$x_{51} + x_{52} + x_{53} + x_{54} \le 1$$
$$x_{11} + x_{21} + x_{31} + x_{41} + x_{51} = 1$$
$$x_{12} + x_{22} + x_{32} + x_{42} + x_{52} = 1$$
$$x_{13} + x_{23} + x_{33} + x_{43} + x_{53} = 1$$
$$x_{14} + x_{24} + x_{34} + x_{44} + x_{54} = 1$$
$$x_{ij} \ge 0$$

41. A plant has four operators to be assigned to four machines. The time (minutes) required by each worker to produce a product on each machine is shown in the following table. Determine the optimal assignment and compute total minimum time.

Operator	Machine			
	A	B	C	D
1	10	12	9	11
2	5	10	7	8
3	12	14	13	11
4	8	15	11	9

42. A shop has four machinists to be assigned to four machines. The hourly cost of having each machine operated by each machinist is as follows.

	Machine			
Machinist	A	B	C	D
1	$12	$11	$8	$14
2	10	9	10	8
3	14	8	7	11
4	6	8	10	9

However, because he does not have enough experience, machinist 3 cannot operate machine B.
   a. Determine the optimal assignment and compute total minimum cost.
   b. Formulate this problem as a general linear programming model.

43. The Omega pharmaceutical firm has five salespersons, whom the firm wants to assign to five sales regions. Given their various previous contacts, the salespersons are able to cover the regions in different amounts of time. The amount of time (days) required by each salesperson to cover each city is shown in the following table. Which salesperson should be assigned to each region to minimize total time? Identify the optimal assignments and compute total minimum time.

	Region				
Salesperson	A	B	C	D	E
1	17	10	15	16	20
2	12	9	16	9	14
3	11	16	14	15	12
4	14	10	10	18	17
5	13	12	9	15	11

44. The Bunker Manufacturing firm has five employees and six machines and wants to assign the employees to the machines to minimize cost. A cost table showing the cost incurred by each employee on each machine follows. Because of union rules regarding departmental transfers, employee 3 cannot be assigned to machine E and employee 4 cannot be assigned to machine B. Solve this problem, indicate the optimal assignment, and compute total minimum cost.

	Machine					
Employee	A	B	C	D	E	F
1	$12	$7	$20	$14	$8	$10
2	10	14	13	20	9	11
3	5	3	6	9	7	10
4	9	11	7	16	9	10
5	10	6	14	8	10	12

45. Given the following cost table for an assignment problem, determine the optimal assignment and compute total minimum cost.

| | Machine | | | |
Operator	A	B	C	D
1	$10	$2	$8	$6
2	9	5	11	9
3	12	7	14	14
4	3	1	4	2

46. An electronics firm produces electronic components, which it supplies to various electrical manufacturers. Quality control records indicate that different employees produce different numbers of defective items. The average number of defects produced by each employee for each of six components is given in the following table. Determine the optimal assignment that will minimize the total average number of defects produced by the firm per month.

| | Component | | | | | |
Employee	A	B	C	D	E	F
1	30	24	16	26	30	22
2	22	28	14	30	20	13
3	18	16	25	14	12	22
4	14	22	18	23	21	30
5	25	18	14	16	16	28
6	32	14	10	14	18	20

47. A dispatcher for the Citywide Taxi Company has six taxicabs at different locations and five customers who have called for service. The mileage from each taxi's present location to each customer is shown in the following table. Determine the optimal assignment(s) that will minimize the total mileage traveled.

| | Customer | | | | |
Cab	1	2	3	4	5
A	7	2	4	10	7
B	5	1	5	6	6
C	8	7	6	5	5
D	2	5	2	4	5
E	3	3	5	8	4
F	6	2	4	3	4

48. The Southeastern Conference has nine basketball officials who must be assigned to three conference games, three to each game. The conference office wants to assign the officials so that the total

distance they travel will be minimized. The distance (in miles) each official would travel to each game is given in the following table.

Official	Game		
	Athens	Columbia	Nashville
1	165	90	130
2	75	210	320
3	180	170	140
4	220	80	60
5	410	140	80
6	150	170	190
7	170	110	150
8	105	125	160
9	240	200	155

Determine the optimal assignment(s) that will minimize the total distance traveled by the officials.

49. In problem 48, officials 2 and 8 have had a recent confrontation with one of the coaches in the game in Athens. They were forced to eject the coach after several technical fouls. The conference office has decided that it would not be a good idea to have these two officials work the Athens game so soon after this confrontation, so they have decided that officials 2 and 8 will not be assigned to the Athens game. How will this affect the optimal solution to this problem?

50. State University has planned six special catered events for the Saturday of its homecoming football game. The events include an alumni brunch, a parent's brunch, a booster club luncheon, a postgame party for season ticket holders, a lettermen's dinner, and a fund-raising dinner for major contributors. The university wants to use local catering firms as well as the university catering service to cater these events and it has asked the caterers to bid on each event. The bids (in $1,000s) based on menu guidelines for the events prepared by the university are shown in the following table.

Caterer	Event					
	Alumni Brunch	Parent's Brunch	Booster Club Lunch	Postgame Party	Lettermen's Dinner	Contributors' Dinner
Al's	$12.6	$10.3	$14.0	$19.5	$25.0	$30.0
Bon Apetít	14.5	13.0	16.5	17.0	22.5	32.0
Custom	13.0	14.0	17.6	21.5	23.0	35.0
Divine	11.5	12.6	13.0	18.7	26.2	33.5
Epicurean	10.8	11.9	12.9	17.5	21.9	28.5
Fouchéss	13.5	13.5	15.5	22.3	24.5	36.0
University	12.5	14.3	16.0	22.0	26.7	34.0

The Bon Apetít, Custom, and University caterers can handle two events, whereas the other four caterers can handle only one. The university is confident all the caterers will do a high-quality job, so it wants to select the caterers for the events that will result in the lowest total cost.

Determine the optimal selection of caterers that will minimize total cost.

51. A university department head has five instructors to be assigned to four different courses. All of the instructors have taught the courses in the past and have been evaluated by the students. The rating for each instructor for each course is given in the following table (a perfect score is 100). The department head wants to know the optimal assignment of instructors to courses that will maximize the overall average evaluation. The instructor who is not assigned to teach a course will be assigned to grade exams.

	Course			
Instructor	A	B	C	D
1	80	75	90	85
2	95	90	90	97
3	85	95	88	91
4	93	91	80	84
5	91	92	93	88

52. The coach of the women's swim team at State University is preparing for the conference swim meet and must choose the four swimmers she will assign to the 800-meter medley relay team. The medley relay consists of four strokes—the backstroke, breaststroke, butterfly, and freestyle. The coach has computed the average times (in minutes) each of her top six swimmers has achieved in each of the four strokes for 200 meters in previous swim meets during the season as follows.

	Stroke (min)			
Swimmer	Backstroke	Breaststroke	Butterfly	Freestyle
Annie	2.56	3.07	2.90	2.26
Beth	2.63	3.01	3.12	2.35
Carla	2.71	2.95	2.96	2.29
Debbie	2.60	2.87	3.08	2.41
Erin	2.68	2.97	3.16	2.25
Fay	2.75	3.10	2.93	2.38

Determine the medley relay team and its total expected relay time for the coach.

53. Biggio's Department Store has six employees available to assign to four departments in the store—home furnishings, china, appliances, and jewelry. Most of the six employees have worked in each of the four departments on several occasions in the past and have demonstrated that they perform better in some departments than in others. The average daily sales for each of the six employees in each of the four departments are shown in the following table.

	Department Sales ($)			
Employee	Home Furnishings	China	Appliances	Jewelry
1	340	160	610	290
2	560	370	520	450
3	270	—	350	420
4	360	220	630	150
5	450	190	570	310
6	280	320	490	360

Employee 3 has not worked in the china department before, so the manager does not want to assign this employee to china.

Determine which employee to assign to each department and indicate the total expected daily sales.

54. The Vanguard Publishing Company has eight college students it hires as salespeople to sell encyclopedias during the summer. The company desires to allocate them to three sales territories. Territory 1 requires three salespeople, and territories 2 and 3 require two salespeople each. It is estimated that each salesperson will be able to generate the amounts of dollar sales per day in each of the three territories as given in the following table. The company desires to allocate the salespeople to the three territories so that sales will be maximized.

Salesperson	Territory		
	1	2	3
A	$110	$150	$130
B	90	120	80
C	205	160	175
D	125	100	115
E	140	105	150
F	100	140	120
G	180	210	160
H	110	120	90

55. Carolina Airlines, a small commuter airline in North Carolina, has six flight attendants that it wants to assign to six monthly flight schedules in a way that will minimize the number of nights they will be away from their homes. The numbers of nights each attendant must be away from home with each schedule are given in the following table. Identify the optimal assignments that will minimize the total number of nights the attendants will be away from home.

Attendant	Schedule					
	A	B	C	D	E	F
1	7	4	6	10	5	8
2	4	5	5	12	7	6
3	9	9	11	7	10	8
4	11	6	8	5	9	10
5	5	8	6	10	7	6
6	10	12	11	9	9	10

56. The football coaching staff at Tech focuses its recruiting on several key states including Georgia, Florida, Virginia, Pennsylvania, New York, and New Jersey. The staff includes seven assistant coaches, two of whom are responsible for Florida, a high school talent-rich state, whereas one coach is assigned to each of the other five states. The staff has been together for a long time and at one time or another all the coaches have recruited all of the states. The head coach has accumulated

some data on the past success rate (i.e., percentage of targeted recruits signed) for each coach in each state as shown in the following table.

Coach	State					
	GA	FL	VA	PA	NY	NJ
Allen	62	56	65	71	55	63
Bush	65	70	63	81	75	72
Crumb	46	53	62	55	64	50
Doyle	58	66	70	67	71	49
Evans	77	73	69	80	80	74
Fouch	68	73	72	80	78	57
Goins	72	60	74	72	62	61

Determine the optimal assignment of coaches to recruiting regions that will maximize the overall success rate and indicate the average percentage success rate for the staff with this assignment.

57. Kathleen Taylor is a freshman at Roanoke College and she wants to develop her schedule for the spring semester. Courses are offered with class periods either on Monday and Wednesday or Tuesday and Thursday for one hour and 15 minutes duration with 15 minutes between class periods. For example, a course designated as 8M meets on Monday and Wednesday from 8:00 A.M. to 9:15 A.M.; the next class on Monday and Wednesday (9M) meets from 9:30 to 10:45; the next class (11M) is from 11:00 A.M. to 12:15 P.M.; and so on. Kathleen wants to take the following six freshman courses with the available sections shown in order of her preference based on the professor who's teaching the course and the time.

Course	Sections Available
Math	11T, 12T, 9T, 11M, 12M, 9M, 8T, 8M
History	11T, 11M, 14T, 14M, 8T, 8M
English	9T, 11T, 14T, 11M, 12T, 14M, 12M, 9M
Biology	14T, 11M, 12M, 14M, 9M, 8T, 8M
Spanish	9T, 11M, 12M, 8T
Psychology	14T, 11T, 12T, 9T, 14M, 8M

For example, there are eight sections of math offered and Kathleen's first preference is for the 11T section, her second choice is the 12T section, and so forth.

a. Determine a class schedule for Kathleen that most closely meets her preferences.
b. Determine a class schedule for Kathleen if she wants to leave 11:00 A.M. to noon open for lunch every day.
c. Suppose Kathleen wants all her classes on two days, either Monday and Wednesday or Tuesday and Thursday. Determine schedules for each and indicate which most closely match her preferences.

THE DEPARTMENT OF MANAGEMENT SCIENCE AND INFORMATION TECHNOLOGY AT TECH

The management science and information technology department at Tech offers between 36 and 40 three-hour course sections each semester. Some of the courses are taught by graduate student instructors, whereas 20 of the course sections are taught by the 10 regular, tenured faculty in the department. Before the beginning of each year the department head sends the faculty a questionnaire asking them to rate their preference for each course using a scale from 1 to 5, where 1 is "strongly preferred," 2 is "preferred but not as strongly as 1," 3 is "neutral," 4 is "prefer not to teach but not strongly," and 5 is "strongly prefer not to teach this course." The faculty have returned their preferences as follows.

Faculty Member	Course							
	3424	3434	3444	3454	4434	4444	4454	4464
Clayton	2	4	1	3	2	5	5	5
Houck	3	3	4	1	2	5	5	4
Huang	2	3	2	1	3	4	4	4
Major	1	4	2	5	1	3	2	2
Moore	1	1	4	4	2	3	3	5
Ragsdale	1	3	1	5	4	1	1	2
Rakes	3	1	2	5	3	1	1	1
Rees	3	4	3	5	5	1	1	3
Russell	4	1	3	2	2	5	5	5
Sumichrast	4	3	1	5	2	3	3	1

For the fall semester the department will offer two sections each of 3424 and 4464; three sections of 3434, 3444, 4434, 4444, and 4454; and one section of 3454.

The normal semester teaching load for a regular faculty member is two sections. (Once the department head determines the courses, he will assign the faculty he schedules the course times so they will not conflict.) Help the department head determine a teaching schedule that will satisfy faculty teaching preferences to the greatest degree possible.

STATELINE SHIPPING AND TRANSPORT COMPANY

Rachel Sundusky is the manager of the South-Atlantic office of the Stateline Shipping and Transport Company. She is in the process of negotiating a new shipping contract with Polychem, a company that manufactures chemicals for industrial use. Polychem wants Stateline to pick up and transport waste products from its six plants to three waste disposal sites. Rachel is very concerned about this proposed arrangement. The chemical wastes that will be hauled can be hazardous to humans and the environment if they leak. In addition, a number of towns and communities in the region where the plants are located prohibit hazardous materials from being shipped through their municipal limits. Thus, not only will the shipments have to be handled carefully and transported at reduced speeds, they will also have to traverse circuitous routes in many cases.

Rachel has estimated the cost of shipping a barrel of waste from each of the six plants to each of the three waste disposal sites as shown in the following table.

Plants	Waste Disposal Sites		
	Whitewater	Los Canos	Duras
Kingsport	$12	$15	$17
Danville	14	9	10
Macon	13	20	11
Selma	17	16	19
Columbus	7	14	12
Allentown	22	16	18

The plants generate the following amounts of waste products each week.

Plant	Waste per Week (bbl)
Kingsport	35
Danville	26
Macon	42
Selma	53
Columbus	29
Allentown	38

The three waste disposal sites at Whitewater, Los Canos, and Duras can accommodate a maximum of 65, 80, and 105 barrels per week, respectively.

In addition to shipping directly from each of the six plants to one of the three waste disposal sites, Rachel is also considering using each of the plants and waste disposal sites as intermediate shipping points. Trucks would be able to drop a load at a plant or disposal site to be picked up and carried on to the final destination by another truck, and vice versa. Stateline would not incur any handling costs because Polychem has agreed to take care of all local handling of the waste materials at the plants and the waste disposal sites. In other words, the only cost Stateline incurs is the actual transportation cost. So Rachel wants to be able to consider the possibility that it may be cheaper to drop and pick up loads at intermediate points rather than shipping them directly.

Rachel estimates the shipping costs per barrel between each of the six plants to be as follows.

Plants	Kingsport	Danville	Macon	Selma	Columbus	Allentown
Kingsport	$—	$6	$4	$9	$7	$8
Danville	6	—	11	10	12	7
Macon	5	11	—	3	7	15
Selma	9	10	3	—	3	16
Columbus	7	12	7	3	—	14
Allentown	8	7	15	16	14	—

The estimated shipping cost per barrel between each of the three waste disposal sites is as follows.

Waste Disposal Site	Whitewater	Los Canos	Duras
Whitewater	$—	$12	$10
Los Canos	12	—	15
Duras	10	15	—

Rachel wants to determine the shipping routes that will minimize Stateline's total cost in order to develop a contract proposal to submit to Polychem for waste disposal. She particularly wants to know if it would be cheaper to ship direct from the plants to the waste sites or if she should drop and pick up some loads at the various plants and waste sites. Develop a model to assist Rachel and solve the model to determine the optimal routes.

BURLINGHAM TEXTILE COMPANY

Brenda Last is the personnel director at the Burlingham Textile Company. The company's plant is expanding, and Brenda must fill five new supervisory positions in carding, spinning, weaving, inspection, and shipping. Applicants for the positions are required to take a written psychological and aptitude test. The test has different modules that indicate an applicant's aptitude and suitability for a specific area and position. For example, one module tests the psychological traits and intellectual skills that are best suited for the inspection department, which are different from the traits and skills required in shipping. Brenda has had ten applicants for the five positions and has compiled the results from the test. The test scores for each position module for each applicant are as follows.

Applicant	Test Module Scores				
	Carding	Spinning	Weaving	Inspection	Shipping
Roger Acuff	68	75	72	86	78
Melissa Ball	73	82	66	78	85
Angela Coe	92	101	90	79	74
Maureen Davis	87	98	75	90	92
Fred Evans	58	62	93	81	75
Bob Frank	93	79	94	92	96
Ellen Gantry	77	92	90	81	93
David Harper	79	66	90	85	86
Mary Inchavelia	91	102	95	90	88
Marilu Jones	72	75	67	93	93

Brenda wants to offer the vacant positions to the five most quali-fied candidates. Determine an optimal assignment for Brenda.

There is a possibility that one or more of the successful appli-cants will turn down a position offer, and Brenda wants to be able to hire the next-best person into a position if someone rejects a job offer. If the applicant selected for the carding job turns it down, whom should Brenda offer this job to next? If the appli-cants for both the carding and spinning jobs turn them down, which of the remaining applicants should Brenda offer each job to? How would a third applicant be selected if three of the job offers are declined?

Brenda believes this is a particularly good group of appli-cants. She would like to retain a few of the people for several more supervisory positions that she believes will open up soon. She has two vacant clerical positions that she can offer to the two best applicants not selected for the five original supervisory positions. Then when the supervisory positions open, she can move these people into them. How should Brenda identify these two people?

CASE PROBLEM

THE GRAPHIC PALETTE

The Graphic Palette is a firm in Charleston, South Carolina, that does graphic artwork and produces color and black-and-white posters, lithographs, and banners. The firm's owners, Kathleen and Lindsey Taylor, have been approached by a client to produce a spectacularly colored poster for an upcoming arts festival. The poster is more complex than anything Kathleen and Lindsey have previously worked on. It requires color screen-ing in three stages, and the processing must proceed rapidly to produce the desired color effect.

By suspending all their other jobs, they can devote three machines to the first stage, four to the second stage, and two to the last stage of the process. Posters that come off the machines at each stage can be processed on any of the machines at the next stage. However, all the machines are different models and of vary-ing ages, so they cannot process the same number of posters in the specified time frame necessary to complete the job. The different machine capacities at each stage are as follows.

Stage 1	Stage 2	Stage 3
Machine 1 = 750	Machine 4 = 530	Machine 8 = 620
Machine 2 = 900	Machine 5 = 320	Machine 9 = 750
Machine 3 = 670	Machine 6 = 450	
	Machine 7 = 250	

Because the machines are of different ages and types, the cost of producing posters on them differs. For example, a poster that starts on machine 1 and then proceeds to machine 4 costs $18. If this poster at machine 4 is then processed on machine 8 it costs an additional $36. The processing costs for each combination of machines for stages 1, 2, and 3 are as follows.

Machine	Machine			
	4	5	6	7
1	18	23	25	21
2	20	26	24	19
3	24	24	22	23

Machine	Machine	
	8	9
4	36	41
5	40	52
6	42	46
7	33	49

Kathleen and Lindsey are unsure how to route the posters from one stage to the next to make as many posters as they possibly can at the lowest cost. Determine how to route the posters through the various stages for the Graphic Palette to minimize costs.

Scheduling at Hawk Systems, Inc.

Jim Huang and Roderick Wheeler were sales representatives in a computer store at a shopping mall in Arlington, Virginia, when they got the idea of going into business in the burgeoning and highly competitive microcomputer market. Jim went to Taiwan over the summer to visit relatives and made a contact with a new firm producing display monitors for microcomputers, which was looking for an East Coast distributor in America. Jim made a tentative deal with the firm to supply a maximum of 500 monitors per month and called Rod to see if he could find a building they could operate out of and some potential customers.

Rod went to work. The first thing he did was send bids to several universities in Maryland, Virginia, and Pennsylvania for contracts as an authorized vendor for monitors at the schools. Next, he started looking for a facility to operate from. Jim and his operation would provide minor physical modifications to the monitors, including some labeling, testing, packaging, and then storage in preparation for shipping. He knew he needed a building with good security, air-conditioning, and a loading dock. However, his search proved to be more difficult than he anticipated. Building space of the type and size he needed was very limited in the area and very expensive. Rod began to worry that he would not be able to find a suitable facility at all. He decided to look for space in the Virginia and Maryland suburbs and countryside; and although he found some good locations, the shipping costs out to these locations were extremely high.

Disheartened by his lack of success, Rod sought help from his sister-in-law Miriam, a local real estate agent. Rod poured out the details of his plight to Miriam over dinner at Rod's mother's house and she was sympathetic. She told Rod that she owned a building in Arlington that might be just what he was looking for, and she would show it to him the next day. As promised, she showed him the ground floor of the building and it was perfect. It had plenty of space, good security, and a nice office; furthermore, it was in an upscale shopping area with lots of goods restaurants. Rod was elated; it was just the type of environment he had envisioned for them to set up their business in. However, his joy soured when he asked Miriam what the rent was. She said she had not worked out the details but the rent would be around $100,000 per year. Rod was shocked, so Miriam said she would offer him an alternative: a storage fee of $10 per monitor for every monitor purchased and in stock the first month of operation with an increase of $2 per month per unit for the remainder of the year. Miriam explained that based on what he told her about the business, they would not have any sales until the universities opened around the end of August or the first of September, and that their sales would fall off to nothing in May or June. She said her offer meant that she would share in their success or failure. If they ended up with some university contracts, she would reap a reward

along with them; if they did not sell many monitors, she would lose on the deal. But in the summer months after school ended, if they had no monitors in stock, they would pay her nothing.

Rod mulled this over and it sounded fair, and he loved the building. Also, he liked the idea that they would not be indebted for a flat lease payment and that the rent was essentially on a per unit basis. If they failed, at least they would not be stuck with a huge lease. So he agreed to Miriam's offer.

When Jim returned from Taiwan, he was skeptical about Rod's lease arrangement with Miriam. He was chagrined that Rod didn't perform a more thorough analysis of the costs, but Rod explained that it was pretty hard to do an analysis when he did not know their costs, potential sales, or selling price. Jim said he had a point, and his concern was somewhat offset by the fact that Rod had gotten contracts with five universities as an authorized vendor for monitors at a selling price of $180 per unit. So the two sat down to begin planning their operation.

First, Jim said he had thought of a name for their enterprise, Hawk Systems, Inc., which he said stood for Huang and Wheeler Computers. When Rod asked how Jim got a *k* out of *computers*, Jim cited poetic license.

Jim said that he had figured that the total cost of the units for them—including the purchase of the units, shipping, and their own material, labor, and administrative costs—would be $100 per unit during the first four months but would then drop to $90 per month for the following four months and, finally, to $85 per month for the remainder of the year. Jim said that the Taiwan firm was anticipating being able to lower the purchase price since its production costs would go down as it gained experience.

Jim thought their own costs would go down, too. He also explained that they would not be able to return any items, so it was important that they develop a good order plan that would minimize costs. This was now much more important than Jim had originally thought because of their peculiar lease arrangement based on their inventory level. Rod said that he had done some research on past computer sales at the universities they had contracted with and had come up with the following sales forecast for the next nine months of the academic year (from September through May):

September	340
October	650
November	420
December	200
January	660
February	550
March	390
April	580
May	120

Rod explained to Jim that computer equipment purchases at universities go up in the fall, then drop until January, and then peak again in April just before university budgets are exhausted at the end of the academic year.

Jim then asked Rod what kind of monthly ordering schedule from Taiwan they should develop to meet demand while minimizing their costs. Rod said that it was a difficult question, but he remembered that when he was in college in a management science course, he had seen a production schedule developed using a transportation model. Jim suggested he get out his old textbook and get busy or they would be turning over all their profits to Miriam.

However, before Rod was able to develop a schedule, Jim got a call from the Taiwan firm saying that it had gotten some more business later in the year and it could no longer supply up to 500 units per month. Instead, it could supply 700 monitors for the first four months and 300 for the next five. Jim and Rod worried about what this would do to their inventory costs.

A. Formulate and solve a transportation model that will determine an optimal monthly ordering and distribution schedule for Hawk Systems that will minimize costs.

B. If Hawk Systems has to borrow approximately $200,000 to start up the business, will it end up making anything the first year?

C. What will the change in the supply pattern from the Taiwan firm cost Hawk Systems?

D. How did Miriam fare with her alternative lease arrangement? Would she have been better off with a flat $100,000 lease payment?

Solutions to Selected Odd-Numbered Problems

1. St. Louis–Chicago = 250, Richmond–Chicago = 50, Richmond–Atlanta = 350, Z = 24,000

3. A3 = 100, B1 = 135, B2 = 45, C2 = 130, C3 = 70, Z = 2,350

5. $x_{11} = 70, x_{13} = 20, x_{22} = 10, x_{23} = 20, x_{32} = 100, x_{43} = 40, Z = 1,240$

7. min. $Z = 14x_{A1} + 9x_{A2} + 16x_{A3} + 18x_{A4} + 11x_{B1} + 8x_{B2} + 100x_{B3} + 16x_{B4} + 16x_{C1} + 12x_{C2} + 10x_{C3} + 22x_{C4}$; s.t. $x_{A1} + x_{A2} + x_{A3} + x_{A4} \le 150, x_{B1} + x_{B2} + x_{B3} + x_{B4} \le 210, x_{C1} + x_{C2} + x_{C3} + x_{C4} \le 320, x_{A1} + x_{B1} + x_{C1} = 130, x_{A2} + x_{B2} + x_{C2} = 70, x_{A3} + x_{B3} + x_{C3} = 180, x_{A4} + x_{B4} + x_{C4} = 240, x_{ij} \ge 0; x_{A2} = 70, x_{A4} = 80, x_{B1} = 50, x_{B4} = 160, x_{C1} = 80, x_{C3} = 180, Z = 8,260$

9. (a) A3 = 90, B1 = 30, B3 = 20, C2 = 80, D1 = 40, D2 = 20, Z = 1,590; alternative: A3 = 90, B1 = 30, B3 = 20, C1 = 40, C2 = 40, D2 = 60, E1 = 50, Z = 1,590

11. 1C = 5, 2C = 10, 3B = 20, 4A = 10, Z = $195; min. $Z = 7x_{1A} + 8x_{1B} + 5x_{1C} + 6x_{2A} + 100x_{2B} + 6x_{2C} + 10x_{3A} + 4x_{3B} + 5x_{3C} + 3x_{4A} + 9x_{4B} + 100x_{4C}$; s.t. $x_{1A} + x_{1B} + x_{1C} \le 5, x_{2A} + x_{2B} + x_{2C} \le 25, x_{3A} + x_{3B} + x_{3C} \le 20, x_{4A} + x_{4B} + x_{4C} \le 25, x_{1A} + x_{2A} + x_{3A} + x_{4A} = 10, x_{1B} + x_{2B} + x_{3B} + x_{4B} = 20, x_{1C} + x_{2C} + x_{3C} + x_{4C} = 15, x_{ij} \ge 0$

13. A2 = 1,800, A4 = 950, A6 = 750, B1 = 1,600, B3 = 1,500, B5 = 1,250, B6 = 650, Z = 3,292.50

15. 1B = 250, 1D = 170, 2A = 520, 2C = 90, 3C = 130, 3D = 210, Z = 21,930

17. 1B = 250, 1D = 170, 2A = 520, 2C = 90, 3C = 130, 3D = 210, TC = $26,430; transportation cost = $21,930, shortage cost = $4,500

19. 1B = 60, 2A = 45, 2B = 25, 2C = 35, 3B = 5, 3D = 65, Z = 1,605

21. NA = 250, SB = 300, SC = 40, EA = 150, EC = 160, WD = 210, CB = 100, CD = 190, Z = 20,700 (multiple optimal)

23. A3 = 8, A4 = 18, B3 = 13, B5 = 27, D3 = 5, D6 = 35, E1 = 25, E2 = 15, E3 = 4, Z = 1,528 (multiple optimal)

25. 17 cases from Albany; $51

27. 1C = 2, 1E = 5, 2C = 10, 3E = 5, 4D = 8, 5A = 9, 6B = 6, Z = 1,275 hr

29. R_J – Jan = 300, O_J – Jan = 110, O_J – Dummy = 90, R_F – FEB = 300, O_F – Feb = 20, O_F – March = 120, O_F – Dummy = 60, R_M – March = 180, R_M – April = 120, O_M – March = 200, R_A – April = 300, O_A – April = 200, R_M – May = 300, O_M – May = 130, O_M – Dummy = 70, R_J – June = 300, O_J – June = 80, O_J – Dummy = 120, Z = 3,010,040

31. Increasing supply at Sacramento, Jacksonville, and Ocala has little effect; increasing supply at San Antonio and Montgomery reduces cost to $242,500

33. Total cost = $1,198,500

35. $x_{14} = 42, x_{15} = 13, x_{26} = 63, x_{35} = 37, x_{48} = 42, x_{59} = 50, x_{67} = 60, x_{68} = 3, Z = 77,362$

37. (a) $x_{14} = 72, x_{25} = 105, x_{34} = 83, x_{46} = 75, x_{47} = 80, x_{56} = 15, x_{58} = 90, Z = 10,043,000$; (b) $x_{14} = 72, x_{25} = 105, x_{34} = 48, x_{35} = 35, x_{46} = 40, x_{47} = 80, x_{56} = 50, x_{58} = 90, Z = 10,043,000$

39. $x_{37} = 2.1, x_{15} = 5.2, x_{26} = 6.3, x_{59} = 5.2, x_{68} = 3.7, x_{69} = 2.6, Z = 27.12 million

41. 1–C, 2–A, 3–B, 4–D, 37 min

43. 1–B, 2–D, 3–A, 4–C, 5–E, 51 days

45. 1–C, 2–A, 3–B, 4–D, $26; alternative solution: 1–D, 2–A, 3–B, 4–C, $26

47. A–3, B–2, C–6, D–1, E–5, F–4, 14 miles; alternative solution: A–6, B–2, C–5, D–3, E–1, F–4, 14 miles

49. 3,6,7–Athens; 1,2,8–Columbia; 4,5,9–Nashville; total mileage = 1,220

51. 1–E, 2–D, 3–B, 4–A, 5–C, 94.5 average

53. 2HF, 3J, 4A, 6C, $1,930

55. 1B, 2A, 3F, 4D, 5C, 6E, 36 nights

57. (a) Math (12T), History (11T), English (9T), Biology (12M), Spanish (11M), Psych (14T), Z = 10; (b) Math (12T), History (14M), English (9T), Biology (12M), Spanish (9M), Psych (14T), Z = 15; (c) not possible

4

Project Management

One of the most popular uses of networks is for project analysis. Such projects as the construction of a building, the development of a drug, or the installation of a computer system can be represented as networks. These networks illustrate the way in which the parts of the project are organized, and they can be used to determine the time duration of the projects. The network techniques that are used for project analysis are CPM and PERT. CPM stands for *critical path method*, and PERT is an acronym for *project evaluation and review technique*. These two techniques are very similar.

There were originally two primary differences between CPM and PERT. With CPM a single, or deterministic, estimate for activity time was used, whereas with PERT probabilistic time estimates were employed. The other difference was related to the mechanics of drawing the project network. In PERT, activities were represented as arcs, or arrowed lines, between two nodes, or circles, whereas in CPM, activities were represented as the nodes or circles. However, these were minor differences, and over time CPM and PERT have been effectively merged into a single technique, conventionally referred to as simply CPM/PERT.

CPM and PERT were developed at approximately the same time (although independently) during the late 1950s. The fact that they have already been so frequently and widely applied attests to their value as management science techniques.

The Elements of Project Management

Management is generally perceived to be concerned with the planning, organization, and control of an ongoing process or activity such as the production of a product or delivery of a service. *Project* management is different in that it reflects a commitment of resources and people to a typically important activity for a relatively short time frame, after which the management effort is dissolved. Projects do not have the continuity of supervision that is typical in the management of a production process. As such, the features and characteristics of project management tend to be somewhat unique. In this section we will discuss the three primary elements of project management: the project team, project planning, and project control.

The Project Team

Project teams are made up of individuals from various areas and departments within a company.

The project team typically consists of a group of individuals selected from other areas in the organization, or from consultants outside the organization, because of their special skills, expertise, and experience related to the project activities. Members of the engineering staff, particularly industrial engineering, are often assigned to project work because of their technical skills. The project team may also include various managers and staff personnel from specific areas related to the project. Even workers can be involved on the project team if their jobs are a function of the project activity. For example, a project team for the construction of a new loading dock facility at a plant might logically include truck drivers, forklift operators, dock workers, and staff personnel and managers from purchasing, shipping, receiving, and packaging, as well as engineers to assess vehicle flow, routes, and space considerations.

Assignment to a project team is usually temporary, and thus can have both positive and negative repercussions. The temporary loss of workers and staff from their permanent jobs can be disruptive for both the employee and the work area. The employee must sometimes "serve two masters," in a sense, reporting to both the project manager and a regular supervisor. Alternatively, because projects are usually "exciting," they provide an opportunity to do work that is new and innovative, and the employee may be reluctant to report back to a more mundane, regular job after the project is completed.

The project manager is often under great pressure.

The most important member of the project team is the *project manager*. The job of managing a project is subject to a great deal of uncertainty and the distinct possibility of failure. Because the project is unique, and usually has not been attempted previously, the outcome is not as certain as the outcome of an ongoing process would be. A degree of security is attained in the supervision of a continuing process that is not present in project management. The project team members are often from diverse areas of the organization and possess different skills, which must be coordinated into a single, focused effort to successfully complete the project. In addition, the project is invariably subject to time and budgetary constraints that are not the same as normal work schedules and resource consumption in an ongoing process. Overall, there is usually more perceived and real pressure associated with project management than in a normal management position. However, there are potential rewards, including the ability to demonstrate one's management abilities in a difficult situation, the challenge of working on a unique project, and the excitement of doing something new.

Project Planning

*A **statement of work** is a written description of the goals, work, and time frame of a project.*

*A **precedence relationship** shows the sequence of activities in a project.*

Planning a project requires that the objectives of the project be clearly defined so that the manager and the team know what is expected. Sometimes this takes the form of a formal written description of what is to be accomplished, the work to be done, and the project time frame, called a *statement of work*. All activities (or steps) in the project must then be completely identified. This is not a simple task because the work involved in the project is new, without a great deal of experiential references to draw upon. An *activity* is the performance of an individual job or work effort that requires labor, resources, and time, and is subject to managerial control or supervision. Once the activities have been identified, their sequential relationship to each other, called a *precedence relationship*—which activities come first, which follow, and so forth—must be determined. In the CPM/PERT technique we discuss later in the chapter, the precedence relationship is visually displayed in the form of a network of activities.

Once the activities of the project have been identified, and their relationship to each other determined in the form of a network or other project planning device, the project activities must be scheduled. This is accomplished by determining estimates of the time required by each activity and then using these estimates to develop an overall project schedule and time to project completion. The estimated project time must be compared with the project objective; if the project time estimate is too long, then means must be sought to reduce project time. This is usually accomplished by assigning more resources or work effort to individual activities to reduce the time they require. This is a topic we will discuss in greater detail in the section on time–cost trade-offs.

Elements of project planning.

To summarize, the elements of the project planning process are as follows.

- Define project objective(s)
- Identify activities
- Establish precedence relationships
- Make time estimates
- Determine project completion time
- Compare project schedule objectives
- Determine resource requirements to meet objectives

for Morgan R. Walker, James E. Kelley Jr., and D. G. Malcolm

In 1956 a research team at E. I. du Pont de Nemours & Company, Inc., led by a du Pont engineer, Morgan R. Walker, and a Remington-Rand computer specialist, James E. Kelley Jr., initiated a project to develop a computerized system to improve the planning, scheduling, and reporting of the company's engineering programs (including plant maintenance and construction projects). The resulting network approach is known as the critical path method (CPM). At virtually the same time the U.S. Navy established a research team composed of members of the Navy Special Projects Office, Lockheed (the prime contractor), and the consulting firm of Booz, Allen, Hamilton, led by D. G. Malcolm, that developed PERT for the design of a management control system for the Polaris Missile Project (a ballistic missile–firing nuclear submarine). The Polaris project eventually included 23 PERT networks encompassing 2,000 events and 3,000 activities.

Project Control

Project management consists of two distinct phases—planning and control. Once the project planning process is completed, the project can be physically initiated—the work involved in the activities can begin. At this point, the focus of project management becomes the control of the actual work involved in the project. Control includes making sure all activities are identified and included, and making sure the activities are completed in the sequence they are supposed to be. Also, resource needs must be identified as work is initiated and completed, and the schedule adjusted to reflect time changes and corrections. However, in most cases primary focus of control is on maintaining the project schedule and making sure the project is completed on time.

*A **work breakdown structure** breaks down a project into subcomponents, components, activities, and tasks.*

The *work breakdown structure* (WBS) is an important methodology for project planning and control. In a WBS a project is broken down into its major subcomponents, referred to as *modules*. These subcomponents are then subdivided into more detailed components, which are further broken down into activities, and finally into individual tasks. The end result is a project organizational structure made up of different levels, with the overall project at the top of the structure and the individual tasks for each activity at the bottom level. The WBS format is a good way to identify activities and to determine the individual task, module, and project workloads and resources required. Further, it helps to identify relationships between modules and activities. It also identifies unnecessary duplication of activities. The modules in the WBS are sometimes used to put together the project network.

Project Networks

The Gantt Chart

*A **Gantt chart** is a graph or bar chart with a bar for each project activity that shows the passage of time.*

A *Gantt chart* is a traditional management technique for scheduling and planning small projects with relatively few activities and precedence relationships. The scheduling technique (also called a *bar chart*) was developed by Henry Gantt, a pioneer in the field of industrial engineering at the artillery ammunition shops of the Frankford Arsenal in 1914. The Gantt chart has been a popular project scheduling tool since its inception and is still widely used today. It is the direct precursor of the CPM/PERT technique, which we will discuss later.

The Gantt chart is a graph with a bar representing time for each activity in the project being analyzed. Figure 1 illustrates a Gantt chart of a simplified project description for building a house. The project contains only seven general activities, such as designing the house, laying the foundation, ordering materials, and so forth. The first activity is "design house and obtain financing," and it requires 3 months to complete, shown by the bar from left to right across the chart. After the first activity is finished, the next two activities, "lay foundation" and "order and receive materials," can start simultaneously. This set of activi-

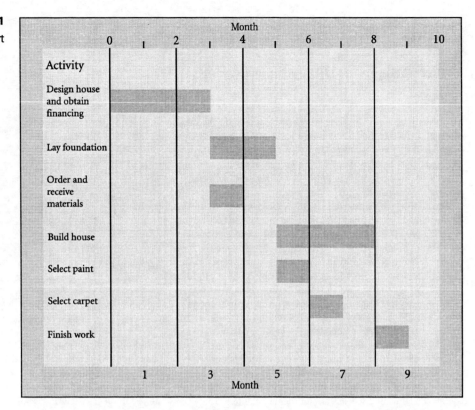

Figure 1
A Gantt chart

ties demonstrates how a precedence relationship works; the design of the house and the financing must precede the next two activities.

The activity "lay foundation" requires 2 months to complete, so it will be finished, at the earliest, at the end of month 5. "Order and receive materials" requires 1 month to complete, and it could be finished after month 4. However, observe that it is possible to delay the start of this activity 1 month until month 4. This delay would still enable the activity to be completed by the end of month 5, when the next activity, "build house," is scheduled to start. This extra time for the activity "order and receive materials" is called *slack*. Slack is the amount by which an activity can be delayed without delaying any of the activities that follow it or the project as a whole. The remainder of the Gantt chart is constructed in a similar manner, and the project is scheduled to be completed at the end of month 9.

The Gantt chart provides a visual display of the project schedule, indicating when activities are scheduled to start, when finished, and where extra time is available and activities can be delayed. The project manager can use the chart to monitor the progress of the activities and see which ones are ahead of schedule and which ones are behind schedule. The Gantt chart also indicates the precedence relationships between activities; however, these relationships are not always easily discernible. This problem is one of the disadvantages of the Gantt chart method, and it limits the chart's use to smaller projects with relatively few activities. The CPM/PERT network technique does not suffer this disadvantage.

Slack is the amount of time an activity can be delayed without delaying the project.

The CPM/PERT Network

A branch represents an activity of a project.

The network flow models in the previous chapter consisted of nodes and branches. The *branches* represented routes (or paths) over which items flowed from one point in the network to other points, which were represented by *nodes*. A CPM/PERT network also consists

Management Science Application

Project "Magic" at Disney Imagineering

The Walt Disney Company theme parks generate $6 billion in revenue each year. Projects for the development of new attractions and rides at the Disney theme parks are unique and challenging, like all operations at Disney. Budgets are tight, schedules are aggressive, and Disney standards for design quality and guest experience are high. It takes more than "pixie dust" to manage a project successfully to completion.

Walt Disney Imagineering (WDI) is the group at Disney that manages and delivers the magic required in its projects. An Imagineering project team is organized to support the special demands of a Disney theme park project. It includes a project manager and show producer, as well as core team members and project control specialists. Each project team is headed by a show producer responsible for the creative vision and a project manager responsible for project scheduling and delivery, plus over 100 specialized work groups in multiple locations including writers, artists, model makers, sculptors, set designers, lighting designers, special effects designers, audio/video designers, show/ride mechanical engineers, show/ride electronic software engineers, show production and tooling specialists, show animators and programmers, graphics designers, architects, film production specialists, interior designers, landscape specialists, and themed painters. These specialty groups must all be coordinated so that they are engaged at the appropriate time and deliver their assigned tasks on time to keep the project on schedule to meet the opening day deadline.

Each new project evolves through a process that establishes the project life cycle and the project schedule. The first phase, *concept*, is the evolutionary phase that is used to ensure that an attraction can be designed to integrate a Disney story line into three dimensions using feasible technology. The next *design* phase includes the complete schematic design for the attraction including the building and show/ride layouts. In the *implementation* phase the show/ride

Photo courtesy of AGE Fotostock America, Inc.

design requirements are completed so that bids can be solicited; show/ride production is started; the facilities are constructed; and the shows and rides are installed, tested, and adjusted. In the final *close out* phase operations training is completed. A fully integrated project master schedule is developed by the project team to successfully deliver the project, based on critical path method (CPM) logic.

The key individual in the project management process is the project manager (PM), who must lead the team to success. The project manager has full accountability for project results. The PM assigns work to divisions and groups, is the project facilitator, must resolve conflicts between team members, and must deal with problems and obstacles from a single, coordinated viewpoint.

Source: Frank Addeman, "Managing the Magic," *PM Network* 13, no. 7 (July 1999): 31–36.

---

*A **node** represents the beginning and end of activities, referred to as events.*

of branches and nodes; however, the branches reflect *activities* of a project or operation, and the nodes represent the beginning and termination of activities, referred to as *events*.

As an example of a CPM/PERT network, we will consider the project of constructing a house. The network for building a house is shown in Figure 2.

Figure 2

Network for building a house

This network consists of three activities: designing the house, obtaining financing, and actually building the house. These activities are represented in the network by arrows (directed branches). The circles (nodes) in Figure 2 reflect events. For example, node 1 is the event of starting to design the house, and node 2 is an event representing the end of designing the house and the beginning of obtaining financing.

The directed branches (arrows) in this network indicate *precedence relationships* among the three activities. In other words, the activity "design house" must precede the activity "obtain financing," which in turn precedes the activity "build house." These precedence relationships must be strictly followed. That is, an activity in this network cannot begin until the preceding activity has been totally completed. In network terminology, we say that when an activity is completed at a node, that node has been *realized*.

When an activity is completed at a node, it has been realized.

The purpose of developing a network is to aid in *planning* and *scheduling* a project. The network for building a house in Figure 2 indicates to the home builder which activities are included in building a house and the order in which the activities must be undertaken. However, scheduling requires that times be associated with the activities. Therefore, we will designate estimated times for the duration of the activities in our home-building network, as shown in Figure 3.

The purpose of a network is to help plan and schedule a project.

Figure 3

Network for building a house with activity times

In the network in Figure 3, the home builder has estimated that financing can be obtained after month 2, the house can be started after month 3, and the entire project can be completed in nine months. Based on this schedule, the home builder can plan when to vacate a present dwelling and move into the new house.

Concurrent Activities

Our home-building example has three activities occurring one after the other. However, a project often includes several activities that can occur at the same time (concurrently). To demonstrate concurrent activities, we will expand our home-building project network as shown in Figure 4.

Figure 4

Expanded network for building a house showing concurrent activities

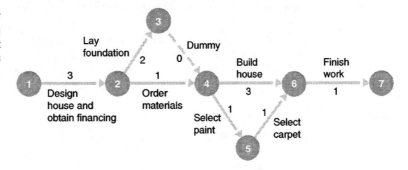

The expanded network in Figure 4 differs in several ways from the project network shown in Figure 2. First, the activities of designing the house and obtaining financing are now combined into activity 1 → 2 (where 1 and 2 are the nodes encompassing this activity). Next, the activity of ordering and receiving building materials follows the first activity. *In addition*, the activity of laying the foundation follows the first activity. In other words, the home builder can have the foundation laid *and* order the materials *concurrently*. Neither of these activities depends on the other; instead, both depend on the completion of the house design and financing.

When the activities of laying the foundation (2 → 3) and ordering materials (2 → 4) are completed, then activities 4 → 5 and 4 → 6 can begin simultaneously. However, before discussing these activities further, we will look more closely at activity 3 → 4, referred to in the network as a *dummy* activity.

A dummy activity is inserted into the network to show a precedence relationship, but it does not represent any actual passage of time. The activities could actually be represented in the network as shown in Figure 5.

*A **dummy** activity is used to show a precedence relationship, but it does not represent a passage of time.*

Figure 5

Concurrent activities

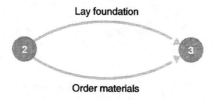

Lay foundation

Order materials

Two or more activities cannot share the same start and end nodes.

In a CPM/PERT network, however, two or more activities are not allowed to share the same starting and ending nodes. (The reason will become apparent later when we develop a schedule for the network.) Therefore, a *dummy* activity (3 → 4) is inserted to give two activities separate end nodes. Notice, though, that a time of zero months has been assigned to activity 3 → 4. Thus, the dummy activity, although it does not represent the passage of time, does show that activity 2 → 3 must be completed prior to any activities beginning at node 4.

Returning to the network (Figure 4), we see that two activities start at node 4. Activity 4 → 6 is the actual building of the house, and activity 4 → 5 is the search for and selection of the paint for the exterior and interior of the house. Activity 4 → 6 and activity 4 → 5 can begin simultaneously and take place concurrently. Following the selection of the paint (activity 4 → 5) and the realization of node 5, the carpet can be selected (because the carpet color is dependent on the paint color). This activity can also occur concurrently with the building of the house (activity 4 → 6). When the building is completed and the paint and carpet are selected, the house can be finished (activity 6 → 7).

The Critical Path

In our simpler network for building a house (before we expanded it), there was a single path with a duration of nine months. However, the expanded network shown in Figure 4 has several paths. In fact, close observation of this network shows four paths, identified in Table 1 and Figure 6.

Table 1

Paths through the house-building network

Path	Events
A	1 → 2 → 3 → 4 → 6 → 7
B	1 → 2 → 3 → 4 → 5 → 6 → 7
C	1 → 2 → 4 → 6 → 7
D	1 → 2 → 4 → 5 → 6 → 7

Figure 6

Alternative paths in the network

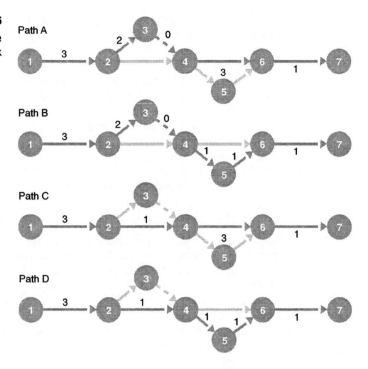

*The **critical path** is the longest path through the network; it is the minimum time the network can be completed.*

The minimum time in which the project can be completed (i.e., the house can be built) is equal to the length of time required by the longest path in the network. The longest path is referred to as the *critical path*. To better understand the relationship between the minimum project time and the longest network path, we will determine the length of each of the four paths shown in Figure 6.

By summing the activity times (shown in Figure 6) along each of the four paths, we can compute the length of each path as follows.

path A:	$1 \rightarrow 2 \rightarrow 3 \rightarrow 4 \rightarrow 6 \rightarrow 7$
	$3 + 2 + 0 + 3 + 1 = 9$ months
path B:	$1 \rightarrow 2 \rightarrow 3 \rightarrow 4 \rightarrow 5 \rightarrow 6 \rightarrow 7$
	$3 + 2 + 0 + 1 + 1 + 1 = 8$ months
path C:	$1 \rightarrow 2 \rightarrow 4 \rightarrow 6 \rightarrow 7$
	$3 + 1 + 3 + 1 = 8$ months
path D:	$1 \rightarrow 2 \rightarrow 4 \rightarrow 5 \rightarrow 6 \rightarrow 7$
	$3 + 1 + 1 + 1 + 1 = 7$ months

Because path A is the longest, it is also the critical path; thus, the minimum completion time for the project is nine months. Now let us analyze the critical path more closely. From Figure 4 we can see that activities $2 \rightarrow 3$ and $2 \rightarrow 4$ cannot start until three months have passed. It is also relatively easy to see that activity $3 \rightarrow 4$ will not start until five months have passed. The start of activities $4 \rightarrow 5$ and $4 \rightarrow 6$ is dependent on two activities leading into node 4. Activity $3 \rightarrow 4$ is completed after five months (which we determine by adding the dummy activity time of zero to the time of five months until node 3 occurs), but activity $2 \rightarrow 4$ is completed at the end of four months. Thus, we have two possible start times for activities $4 \rightarrow 5$ and $4 \rightarrow 6$, five months and four months. However, because no activity starting at node 4 can occur until all preceding activities have been finished, the soonest node 4 can be realized is five months.

Now let us consider the activities leading from node 4. Using the same logic as on the previous page, we can see that activity 6 → 7 cannot start until after eight months (five months at node 4 plus the three months required by activity 4 → 6) or after seven months (five months at node 4 plus the two months required by activities 4 → 5 and 5 → 6). Because all activities ending at node 6 must be completed before activity 6 → 7 can start, the soonest they can occur is eight months. Adding one month for activity 6 → 7 to the time at node 6 gives a project duration of nine months. Recall that this is the time of the longest path in the network, or the critical path.

This brief analysis demonstrates the concept of a critical path and the determination of the minimum completion time of a project. However, this was a cumbersome method for determining a critical path. Next, we will discuss a mathematical approach for scheduling the project activities and determining the critical path.

Activity Scheduling

ES *is the earliest time an activity can start.*

EF *is the earliest start time plus the activity time.*

In our analysis of the critical path, we determined the soonest time that each activity could be finished. For example, we found that the earliest time activity 4 → 5 could start was five months. This time is referred to as the *earliest start time*, and it is expressed symbolically as *ES*. To determine the earliest start time for every activity, we make a *forward pass* through the network. That is, we start at the first node and move forward through the network. The earliest time for an activity is the maximum time that all preceding activities have been completed—the time when the activity start node is realized.

The *earliest finish time, EF*, for an activity is the earliest start time plus the activity time estimate. For example, if the earliest start time for activity 1 → 2 is at time 0, then the earliest finish time is three months. In general, the earliest start and finish times for an activity $i → j$ are computed according to the following mathematical relationship.

$$ES_{ij} = \text{Maximum } (EF_i)$$
$$EF_{ij} = ES_{ij} + t_{ij}$$

The earliest start and earliest finish times for all the activities in our project network are shown in Figure 7. The earliest start time for the first activity in the network (for which there are no predecessor activities) is always zero, or $ES_{12} = 0$. This enables us to compute the earliest finish time for activity 1 → 2 as

$$EF_{12} = ES_{12} + t_{12} = 0 + 3 = 3 \text{ months}$$

Figure 7
Earliest activity start and finish times

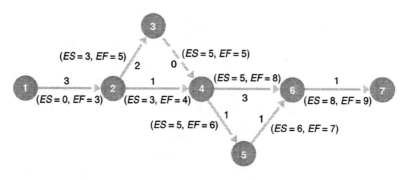

The earliest start for activity 2 → 3 is next computed,

$$ES_{23} = \text{Max } EF_2 = 3 \text{ months}$$

and the corresponding earliest finish time is

$$EF_{23} = ES_{23} + t_{23} = 3 + 2 = 5 \text{ months}$$

For activity $3 \rightarrow 4$ the earliest start time (ES_{34}) is five months and the earliest finish time (EF_{34}) is five months; for activity $2 \rightarrow 4$ the earliest start time (ES_{24}) is three months and the earliest finish time (EF_{24}) is four months.

Now consider activity $4 \rightarrow 6$, which has two predecessor activities. The earliest start time is computed as

$$ES_{46} = \text{Max } EF_4 = \text{Max } (5, 4) = 5 \text{ months}$$

and the earliest finish time is

$$EF_{46} = ES_{46} + t_{46} = 5 + 3 = 8 \text{ months}$$

All the remaining earliest start and finish times are computed similarly. Notice in Figure 7 that the earliest finish time for activity $6 \rightarrow 7$, the last activity in the network, is 9, which is the total project duration, or critical path time.

Companions to the earliest start and finish are the *latest start* and *finish* times. The latest start time is the latest time an activity can start without delaying the completion of the project beyond the project critical path time. For our example, the project completion time (and earliest finish time) at node 7 is nine months. Thus, the objective of determining latest times is to see how long each activity can be delayed without the project exceeding nine months.

In general, the latest start and finish times for an activity $i \rightarrow j$ are computed according to the following formulas.

$$LS_{ij} = LF_{ij} - t_{ij}$$
$$LF_{ij} = \text{Minimum } (LS_j)$$

The term "Minimum (LS_j)" means the minimum latest start time for all activities leaving node j. Whereas a forward pass through the network is made to determine the earliest times, the latest times are computed using a backward pass. We start at the end of the network at node 7 and work backward, computing the latest times for each activity. Because we want to determine how long each activity in the network can be delayed without extending the project time, the latest finish time at node 7 cannot exceed the earliest finish time. Therefore, the latest finish time at node 7 is nine months. This and all other latest times are shown in Figure 8.

Figure 8

Latest activity start and finish times

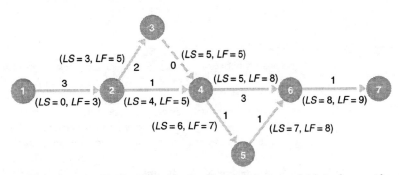

Starting at the end of the network, the critical path time, which is also equal to the earliest finish time of activity $6 \rightarrow 7$, is nine months. This automatically becomes the latest finish time for activity $6 \rightarrow 7$, or

$$LF_{67} = 9 \text{ months}$$

Using this value, the latest start time for activity $6 \rightarrow 7$ can be computed.

$$LS_{67} = LF_{67} - t_{67} = 9 - 1 = 8 \text{ months}$$

The latest finish time for activity $5 \rightarrow 6$ is the minimum of the latest start times for the activities leaving node 6. Because activity $6 \rightarrow 7$ leaves node 6, the latest start time is computed as follows.

$$LF_{56} = \text{Min } (LS_6) = 8 \text{ months}$$

The latest start time for activity $5 \rightarrow 6$ is

$$LS_{56} = LF_{56} - t_{56} = 8 - 1 = 7 \text{ months}$$

For activity $4 \rightarrow 6$, the latest finish time (LF_{46}) is eight months and the latest start time (LS_{46}) is five months; for activity $4 \rightarrow 5$, the latest finish time (LF_{45}) is seven months and the latest start time (LS_{45}) is six months.

Now consider activity $2 \rightarrow 4$, which has two activities following it. The latest finish time is computed as follows.

$$LF_{24} = \text{Min } (LS_4) = \text{Min } (5, 6) = 5 \text{ months}$$

The latest start time is computed as

$$LS_{24} = LF_{24} - t_{24} = 5 - 1 = 4 \text{ months}$$

All the remaining latest start and latest finish times are computed similarly. Figure 9 includes the earliest and latest start times, and earliest and latest finish times for all activities.

Figure 9
Earliest activity start and finish times

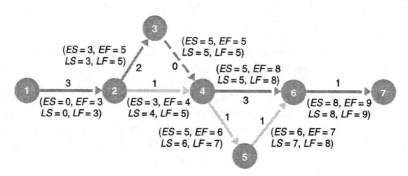

Activity Slack

The project network in Figure 9 with all activity start and finish times highlights the critical path $(1 \rightarrow 2 \rightarrow 3 \rightarrow 4 \rightarrow 6 \rightarrow 7)$ we determined earlier by inspection. Notice that for the activities on the critical path, the earliest start times and latest start times are equal. This means that these activities on the critical path must start exactly on time and cannot be delayed at all. If the start of any activity on the critical path is delayed, then the overall project time will be increased. As a result, we now have an alternative way to determine the critical path besides simply inspecting the network. The activities on the critical path can be determined by seeing for which activities $ES = LS$ or $EF = LF$. In Figure 9, the activities $1 \rightarrow 2, 2 \rightarrow 3, 3 \rightarrow 4, 4 \rightarrow 6$, and $6 \rightarrow 7$ all have earliest start times that are equal (and $EF = LF$); thus, they are on the critical path.

Slack is the amount of time an activity can be delayed without delaying the project.

For those activities not on the critical path the earliest and latest start times (or earliest and latest finish times) are not equal, and *slack* time exists. Slack is the amount of time an activity can be delayed without affecting the overall project duration. In effect, it is extra time available for completing an activity.

Slack, S_{ij}, is computed using either of the following formulas,

$$S_{ij} = LS_{ij} - ES_{ij}$$

or

$$S_{ij} = LF_{ij} - EF_{ij}$$

For example, the slack for activity $2 \rightarrow 4$ is computed as follows.

$$S_{24} = LS_{24} - ES_{24} = 4 - 3 = 1 \text{ month}$$

If the start of activity $2 \rightarrow 4$ were delayed for one month, the activity could still be completed by month 5 without delaying the project completion time. The slack for each activity in our example project network is shown in Table 2 and in Figure 10.

Table 2

Activity slack

Activity	LS	ES	LF	EF	Slack, S
*1 → 2	0	0	3	3	0
2 → 3	3	3	5	5	0
2 → 4	4	3	5	4	1
*3 → 4	5	5	5	5	0
4 → 5	6	5	7	6	1
*4 → 6	5	5	8	8	0
5 → 6	7	6	8	7	1
*6 → 7	8	8	9	9	0

*Critical path activities

Figure 10

Activity slack

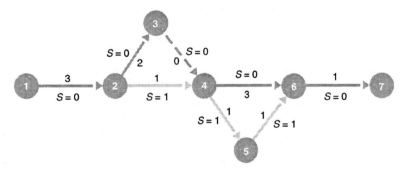

Inspection of Table 2 shows that there is no slack for the activities on the critical path (marked with an asterisk). All other activities not on the critical path do have slack.

Before we conclude our discussion of slack, we will discuss one additional matter. Notice that activity $4 \rightarrow 5$ or $5 \rightarrow 6$ in Figure 10 can be delayed one month, but both activities cannot each be delayed one month. If activity $4 \rightarrow 5$ starts at month 6 instead of 5, then it will be completed at month 7, which will not allow the start of activity $5 \rightarrow 6$ to be delayed. The opposite is also true. If $4 \rightarrow 5$ starts at month 5, activity $5 \rightarrow 6$ can be delayed one month. The slack on these two activities is referred to as *shared slack*. This means that the sequence of activities $4 \rightarrow 5 \rightarrow 6$ can be delayed one month jointly without delaying the project. Slack is obviously beneficial to the project manager because it enables resources to be temporarily pulled away from activities with slack and used for other activities that might be delayed for various reasons, or for which the time estimate has proven to be inaccurate.

Shared slack is available for a sequence of activities.

The times for the network activities are simply estimates for which there is usually not a lot of historical basis (since projects tend to be unique undertakings). As such, activity time estimates are subject to quite a bit of uncertainty. However, the uncertainty inherent in activity time estimates can be reflected to a certain extent by using probabilistic time estimates instead of the single, deterministic estimates we have used so far.

Probabilistic Activity Times

In the project network for building a house presented in the previous section, all of the activity time estimates were single values. By using only a single activity time estimate, we are, in effect, assuming that activity times are known with certainty (i.e., they are deterministic). For example, in Figure 4, the time estimate for activity $2 \rightarrow 3$ (laying the foundation) is shown to be two months. Because only this one value is given, we must assume that the activity time does not vary (or varies very little) from two months. In reality, however, it is rare that activity time estimates can be made with certainty. Projects that are networked are particularly likely to be unique, and thus there is little historical evidence that can be used as a basis to predict future occurrences. However, recall that we earlier indicated one of the primary differences between CPM and PERT was that PERT used probabilistic activity times. It is this approach to estimating activity times for a project network that we discuss in this section.

To demonstrate the use of probabilistic activity times, we will employ a new example. (We could use the house-building network of the previous section; however, a network that is a little larger and more complex will provide more experience with different types of projects.) The Southern Textile Company has decided to install a new computerized order processing system. In the past, orders for the cloth the company produces were processed manually, which contributed to delays in delivering orders and resulted in lost sales. The company wants to know how long it will take to install the new system.

The network for the installation of the new order processing system is shown in Figure 11. We will briefly describe the activities.

The network begins with three concurrent activities: The new computer equipment is installed (activity $1 \rightarrow 2$); the computerized order processing system is developed (activity $1 \rightarrow 3$); and people are recruited to operate the system (activity $1 \rightarrow 4$). Once people are hired, they are trained for the job (activity $4 \rightarrow 5$); and other personnel in the company, such as marketing, accounting, and production personnel, are informed about the new system (activity $4 \rightarrow 8$). Once the system is developed (activity $1 \rightarrow 3$), it is tested manually to make sure that it is logical (activity $3 \rightarrow 5$). Following activity $1 \rightarrow 2$, the new equipment is tested and corrected (activity $2 \rightarrow 6$), and the newly trained personnel begin training on the computerized system (activity $5 \rightarrow 7$). Also, event 5 begins the testing of the system on the computer to check for errors (activity $5 \rightarrow 8$). The final activities include a trial run and changeover to the system (activity $7 \rightarrow 9$) and final debugging of the computer system (activity $6 \rightarrow 9$).

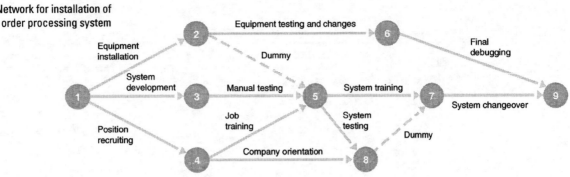

Figure 11

Network for installation of order processing system

At this stage in a project network, we previously assigned a single time estimate to each network activity. In a PERT project network, however, we determine *three time estimates* for each activity, which will enable us to estimate the mean and variance for *a beta distribution* of the activity times. We are assuming that the activity times can be described by a beta distribution for several reasons. First, the beta distribution mean and variance can be approximated with three estimates. Second, the beta distribution is continuous, but it has no predetermined shape (such as the bell shape of the normal curve). It will take on the shape indicated—that is, be skewed—by the time estimates given. This is beneficial, because typically we have no prior knowledge of the shapes of the distributions of activity times in a unique project network. Third, although other types of distributions have been shown to be no more or less accurate than the beta, it has become traditional to use the beta distribution for probabilistic network analysis.

The three time estimates for each activity are the most likely time, the optimistic time, and the pessimistic time. The *most likely time* is the time that would most frequently occur if the activity were repeated many times. The *optimistic time* is the shortest possible time within which the activity could be completed if everything went right. The *pessimistic time* is the longest possible time the activity would require to be completed assuming everything went wrong. In general, the person most familiar with an activity makes these estimates to the best of his or her knowledge and ability. In other words, the estimate is subjective.

*Three time estimates for each activity—a **most likely**, an **optimistic** and a **pessimistic**—provide an estimate of the mean and variance of a beta distribution.*

These three time estimates can subsequently be used to estimate the mean and variance of a beta distribution. If we let

$$a = \text{optimistic time estimate}$$
$$m = \text{most likely time estimate}$$
$$b = \text{pessimistic time estimate}$$

then the mean and variance are computed as follows.

$$\text{mean (expected time): } t = \frac{a + 4m + b}{6}$$

$$\text{variance: } v = \left(\frac{b-a}{6}\right)^2$$

These formulas provide a reasonable estimate of the mean and variance of the beta distribution, a distribution that is continuous and can take on various shapes—that is, exhibit skewness.

141

The three time estimates, the mean, and the variance for all the activities in the network shown in Figure 11 are given in Table 3.

Table 3
Activity time estimates for Figure 11

| Activity | Time Estimates (weeks) | | | Time | Mean Variance |
	a	m	b	t	v
1 → 2	6	8	10	8	4/9
1 → 3	3	6	9	6	1
1 → 4	1	3	5	3	4/9
2 → 5	0	0	0	0	0
2 → 6	2	4	12	5	25/9
3 → 5	2	3	4	3	1/9
4 → 5	3	4	5	4	1/9
4 → 8	2	2	2	2	0
5 → 7	3	7	11	7	16/9
5 → 8	2	4	6	4	4/9
8 → 7	0	0	0	0	0
6 → 9	1	4	7	4	1
7 → 9	1	10	13	9	4

As an example of the computation of the individual activity mean times and variances, consider activity $1 \to 2$. The three time estimates ($a = 6$, $m = 8$, $b = 10$) are substituted in our formulas as follows.

$$t = \frac{a + 4m + b}{6} = \frac{6 + 4(8) + 10}{6} = 8 \text{ weeks}$$

$$v = \left(\frac{b - a}{6}\right)^2 = \left(\frac{10 - 6}{6}\right)^2 = \frac{4}{9} \text{ weeks}$$

The other values for the mean and variance in Table 3 are computed similarly. All of the means and variances for the activities in our example network are shown in Figure 12.

Figure 12
Network with mean activity times and variances

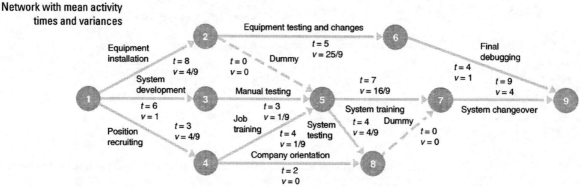

Once the expected activity times have been computed for each activity, we can determine the critical path the same way we did previously, except that we use the expected activity times, *t*. Recall that in the project network we identified the critical path as the one containing those activities with zero slack. This requires the determination of earliest and latest event times, as shown in Figure 13 and Table 4.

Figure 13
Earliest and latest activity times

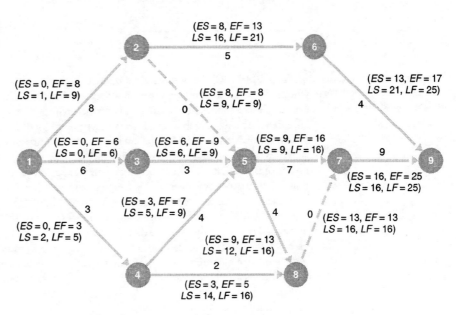

Table 4
Activity earliest and latest times and slack

Activity	t	σ^2	ES	EF	LS	LF	S
1 → 2	8	0.44	0	8	1	9	1
1 → 3	6	1.00	0	6	0	6	0
1 → 4	3	0.44	0	3	2	5	2
2 → 5	0	0.00	8	8	9	9	1
2 → 6	5	2.78	8	13	16	21	8
3 → 5	3	0.11	6	9	6	9	0
4 → 5	4	0.11	3	7	5	9	2
4 → 8	2	0.00	3	5	14	16	11
5 → 7	7	1.78	9	16	9	16	0
5 → 8	4	0.44	9	13	12	16	3
8 → 7	0	0.00	13	13	16	16	3
6 → 9	4	1.00	13	17	21	25	8
7 → 9	8	4.00	16	25	16	25	0

The critical path has no slack.

The project variance is the sum of the variance of the critical path activities.

Observing Table 4, we can see that the critical path encompasses activities 1 → 3 → 5 → 7 → 9, because these activities have no available slack. We can also see that the *expected* project completion time (t_p) is 25 weeks. However, it is possible to compute the variance for project completion time. To determine the project variance, we *sum the variances for those activities on the critical path*. Using the variances computed in Table 3 and the critical path activities shown in Figure 13, we can compute the variance for project duration (v_p) as follows.

Critical Path Activity	Variance
$1 \rightarrow 3$	1
$3 \rightarrow 5$	1/9
$5 \rightarrow 7$	16/9
$7 \rightarrow 9$	4
	62/9

$$v_p = 62/9 = 6.9 \text{ weeks}$$

The expected project time is assumed to be normally distributed based on the central limit theorem.

The CPM/PERT method assumes that the activity times are statistically independent, which allows us to sum the individual expected activity times and variances to get an expected *project* time and variance. It is further assumed that the network mean and variance are normally distributed. This assumption is based on the central limit theorem of probability, which for CPM/PERT analysis and our purposes states that if the number of activities is large enough and the activities are statistically independent, then the sum of the means of the activities along the critical path will approach the mean of a normal distribution. For the small examples in this chapter, it is questionable whether there are sufficient activities to guarantee that the mean project completion time and variance are normally distributed. Although it has become conventional in CPM/PERT analysis to employ probability analysis using the normal distribution regardless of the network size, the prudent user of CPM/PERT analysis should bear this limitation in mind.

Given these assumptions, we can interpret the expected project time (t_p) and variance (v_p) as the mean (μ) and variance (σ^2) of a normal distribution:

$$\mu = 25 \text{ weeks}$$
$$\sigma^2 = 6.9 \text{ weeks}$$

In turn, we can use these statistical parameters to make various probabilistic statements about the project.

Probability Analysis of the Project Network

Using the normal distribution, probabilities can be determined by computing the number of standard deviations (Z) a value is from the mean, as illustrated in Figure 14.

Figure 14

Normal distribution of network duration

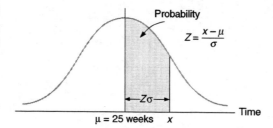

The value, Z, is computed using the following formula.

$$Z = \frac{x - \mu}{\sigma}$$

This value is then used to find the corresponding probability in the table of "Normal Curve Areas" in the appendix.

For example, suppose the textile company manager told customers that the new order processing system would be completely installed in 30 weeks. What is the probability that it will, in fact, be ready by that time? This probability is illustrated as the shaded area in Figure 15.

Figure 15

Probability the network will be completed in 30 weeks or less

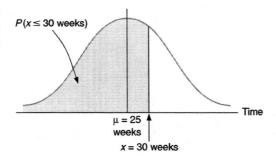

To compute the Z value for a time of 30 weeks we must first compute the standard deviation (σ) from the variance (σ^2).

$$\sigma^2 = 6.9$$
$$\sigma = \sqrt{6.9} = 2.63$$

Next, we substitute this value for the standard deviation along with the value for the mean and our proposed project completion time (30 weeks) into the following formula.

$$Z = \frac{x - \mu}{\sigma}$$
$$= \frac{30 - 25}{2.63} = 1.90$$

A Z value of 1.90 corresponds to a probability of .4713 in the table of "Normal Curve Areas" in the appendix. This means that there is a .9713 (.5000 + .4713) probability of completing the project in 30 weeks or less.

Suppose one customer, frustrated with delayed orders, has told the textile company that if the new ordering system is not working within 22 weeks, she will trade elsewhere. The probability of the project's being completed within 22 weeks is computed as follows.

$$Z = \frac{22 - 25}{2.63}$$
$$= \frac{-3}{2.63} = -1.14$$

A Z value of 1.14 (the negative is ignored) corresponds to a probability of .3729 in the table of "Normal Curve Areas" in the appendix. Thus, there is only a .1271 probability that the customer will be retained, as illustrated in Figure 16.

Figure 16

Probability the network will be
completed in 22 weeks or less

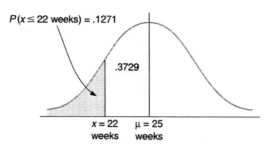

$P(x \le 22 \text{ weeks}) = .1271$

.3729

$x = 22$ weeks $\mu = 25$ weeks

Management Science Application

The Mars Pathfinder *Project*

Since the early days of U.S. space exploration, project management has played a crucial role in its success. Engineers, scientists,
and managers at NASA and related agencies and organizations have
used project management techniques to develop, manage, and control sophisticated projects that have not only brought back valuable
information about space but also resulted in technological advances
on Earth. One of the most significant and widely publicized of these
projects was the Mars *Pathfinder* project.

On July 4, 1997, the Mars *Pathfinder* spacecraft successfully
landed on the surface of Mars. The following day the Sojourner
rover rolled down its deployment ramp and began to traverse the
surface. During its nearly three months of operation on Mars the
Sojourner and Sagan Memorial Station transmitted nearly 2.6
gigabits of science and engineering data including 16,000 camera
images from the lander and 550 images from the rover; 8.5 million
temperature, pressure, and wind measurements; 16 separate
chemical measurements of rocks and soil; and the results of 10
technology experiments on the rover.

The mission was conceived as an engineering demonstration
of a reliable, low-cost system for delivering payloads to the surface
of Mars, and focusing primarily on scientific objectives. NASA
initiated the project with the desire for "better, faster, cheaper"
missions with a maximum three-year development period and a
cost cap of $150 million.

Maintaining the launch schedule was an extremely critical
aspect of the project due to the orbital relationship between Earth
and Mars. The 30-day launch window necessary for a successful
trajectory to Mars occurs only once every 26 months, so a schedule slip of more than 30 days would mean a 26-month delay in the
launch. The flight system manager and the project scheduler
maintained the project schedule carefully tracking critical project
events and milestones. The actual launch took place on December
4, 1996, the third day of the targeted launch window.

Photo courtesy of **CORBIS BETTMAN**

Another significant challenge was the management of costs
and resources. The baseline budget for project development of
$131 million with $40 million held in reserve was based on a
product-oriented work breakdown structure (WBS) and was formalized in July 1993. The actual development cost was approximately $400,000 less than the NASA cost cap of $150 million. By
contrast the two *Viking* missions, which landed on Mars in 1976,
had a six-year development period and cost $915 million (equiva-
lent to $3 billion in 1992 dollars). The Mars *Pathfinder* project met
all of its technical challenges, was completed on schedule, and
under the NASA cost cap, and proved that planetary missions
could succeed in a "better, faster, cheaper" environment.

Source: C. Sholes and N. Chalfin, "Mars *Pathfinder* Project: 1998
International Project of the Year," *PM Network* 13, no. 1 (January
1999): 30–35.

CPM/PERT Analysis with QM for Windows

The capability to perform CPM/PERT network analysis is a standard feature of most management science software packages for the personal computer. To illustrate the application of QM for Windows we will use our example of installing an order processing system at the Southern Textile Company. The QM for Windows solution output is shown in Exhibit 1.

Exhibit 1

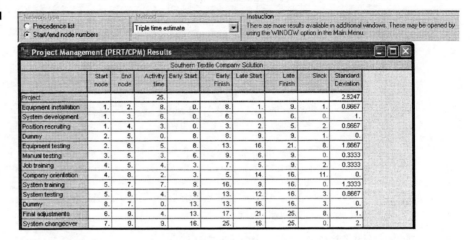

	Start node	End node	Activity time	Early Start	Early Finish	Late Start	Late Finish	Slack	Standard Deviation
Project			25.						2.6247
Equipment installation	1.	2.	8.	0.	8.	1.	9.	1.	0.6667
System development	1.	3.	6.	0.	6.	0.	6.	0.	1.
Position recruiting	1.	4.	3.	0.	3.	2.	5.	2.	0.6667
Dummy	2.	5.	0.	8.	8.	9.	9.	1.	0.
Equipment testing	2.	6.	5.	8.	13.	16.	21.	8.	1.6667
Manual testing	3.	5.	3.	6.	9.	6.	9.	0.	0.3333
Job training	4.	5.	4.	3.	7.	5.	9.	2.	0.3333
Company orientation	4.	8.	2.	3.	5.	14.	16.	11.	0.
System training	5.	7.	7.	9.	16.	9.	16.	0.	1.3333
System testing	5.	8.	4.	9.	13.	12.	16.	3.	0.6667
Dummy	8.	7.	0.	13.	13.	16.	16.	3.	0.
Final adjustments	6.	9.	4.	13.	17.	21.	25.	8.	1.
System changeover	7.	9.	9.	16.	25.	16.	25.	0.	2.

Notice that the project duration of 25 weeks is shown at the top of the fourth column under "Activity Time". The critical path is identified by those activities with 0 slack. Also notice that QM for Windows provides the standard deviation rather than the variance for each activity.

Activity-on-Node Networks and Microsoft Project

So far we have developed project networks using only the "activity-on-arrow" (AOA) convention; however, there is an alternative network approach called activity-on-node (AON). In this method of drawing networks the activities are placed on the nodes and the arrows (or branches) indicate the precedence relationships between activities. The two conventions accomplish the same thing but there are a few minor differences. An AON network will often have more nodes than an AOA network. Also, an AON network does not require dummy activities because two "activities" will never have the same start and end nodes.

For our purposes there is another, more important difference between the two methods. While most project management computer software programs can handle either convention, *Microsoft Project* does not; it handles only AON networks. Because we want to demonstrate project management using the popular Microsoft Project software, we must first show how AON networks are constructed.

The AON Network Convention

We will demonstrate how to draw an activity-on-node network using the example of the house-building project we first constructed in Figure 4. Figure 17 shows the node structure for the first activity in this example network, "designing the house and obtaining financing." This node includes the activity number in the upper left-hand corner, the activity duration in the lower left-hand corner, and the earliest start and finish times, and latest start and finish times in the four boxes on the right side of the node. The earliest and latest times for the activity are computed using the same formulas we used originally with the AOA network.

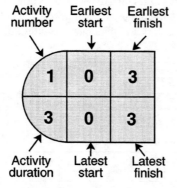

Activity-on-node configuration

The complete network for the house-building project is shown in Figure 18. Notice that the arrows indicate only the preference relationships between activities on the nodes. For example, the two arrows ending at node 5 show that activities 2 and 3 must be completed before activity 5 may begin. Also notice that the dummy activity in Figure 4 is not included in this network.

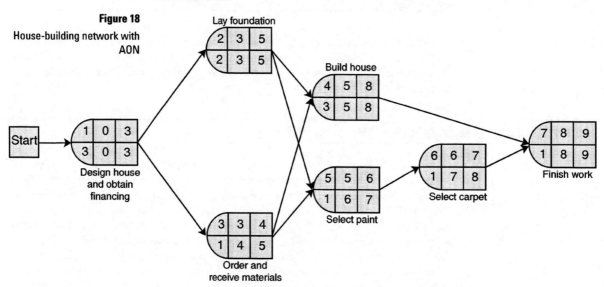

Figure 18
House-building network with AON

Slack on each of the activities is computed the same as on the AOA network by subtracting the earliest start time (*ES*) from the latest start time (*LS*) or the earliest finish time (*EF*) from the latest finish time (*LF*). For example, the slack on node 5 is one month (i.e., $LS - ES = 6 - 5 = 1$).

Microsoft Project

As we mentioned, Microsoft Project is a very popular and widely used software package for project management. It is also relatively easy to use. We will demonstrate how to use Microsoft Project using the AON project network in Figure 18. Exhibit 2 shows the initial spreadsheet screen that appears when you open Microsoft Project. The Microsoft Project software includes a tutorial that carefully leads the user through the detailed steps of using the program. In this discussion we will present a brief overview of the steps required to create a project network.

Exhibit 2

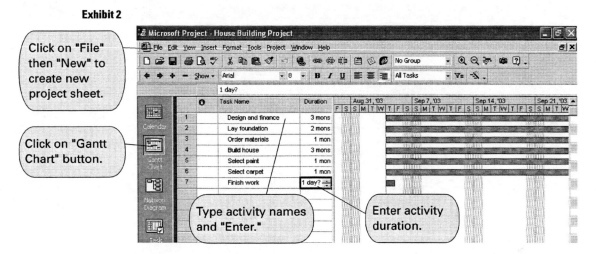

First, a new "project book" or project screen can be generated by clicking on the "File" button on the toolbar and then clicking on "New." When the new screen comes up you can "Save" it with your project name; in this example the project name is "House Building Project." The program requires that you provide a start date for the project. When you open a new file a "Project Information" window appears in which you can designate a project start date and (if you wish) end date. For this example we have arbitrarily entered a start date of September 4, 2003. The "Project Information" window can also be accessed from the "Project" button on the toolbar at the top of the screen.

When the initial screen appears as in Exhibit 2, click on the "Gantt Chart" button on the left side of the screen. Then in the blanks under "Task Name" enter each of the activity (or task) descriptions. After you "Enter" a name the cursor will shift to the cell under "Duration", in which the project duration is typed with the appropriate time unit, that is, "d" for days, "w" for weeks, "mon" for months, and so on. For example, for the activity "Design and finance" "3 mons" is typed in. Notice that the bars to the right of the task names and durations are for the Gantt chart; however, the Gantt chart cannot be developed yet because the precedence relationships have not yet been designated for the activities.

The precedence relationships between predecessor and successor activities are designated as follows. Holding the "Ctrl" button down first click on an activity (i.e., a task), for example, "Design and finance," and then click on a successor activity, for example, "Lay foundation." (Be sure the "Ctrl" button is held down for both.) Then click on the "Link" button on the toolbar. This is shown in Exhibit 3. This creates the precedence relationship between these two activities. This step must be repeated for all of the precedence relationships between activities in the project. Exhibit 3 shows the precedence relationships and the completed Gantt chart (on the right of the screen) for the entire project.

Notice in Exhibit 3 that the "Start" and "Finish" times are provided. The finish time is Wednesday, May 12, 2004.

In order to see the AON project network click on the "Network Diagram" button on the left side of the screen. Exhibit 4 shows the project network for this example. The critical path is determined by clicking on the "Format" button on the toolbar at the top of the screen and then clicking on the "Gantt Chart Wizard." A "Gantt Chart Wizard" window appears and from there the critical path can be activated.

Exhibit 3

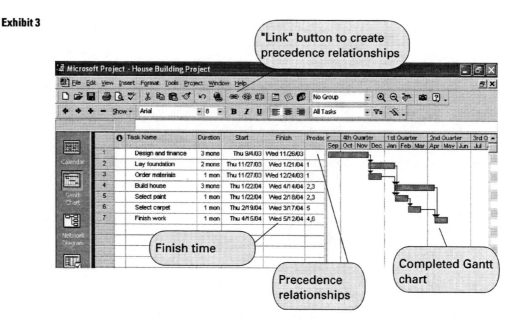

Exhibit 4

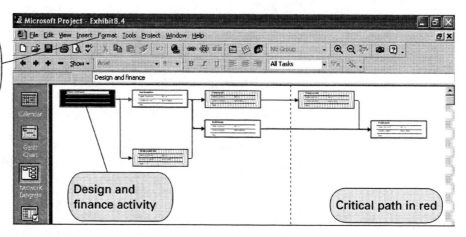

The network in Exhibit 4 has been reduced in size in order to be able to show it all on one screen in the exhibit display; however, the writing inside the nodes is too small to be legible. Exhibit 5 shows the nodes as they would appear on the computer screen if they were normal size.

This provides a very brief overview of the basic Microsoft Project capabilities. The program is capable of much more, including detailed project scheduling, resource and cost allocations, and budgeting, as well as a variety of chart and display options. The program also has the capability to develop work breakdown structures (WBS).

Project Crashing and Time—Cost Trade-off

To this point we have demonstrated the use of CPM and PERT network analysis for determining project time schedules. This in itself is valuable to the manager planning a project. However, in addition to scheduling projects, the project manager is frequently confronted

Exhibit 5

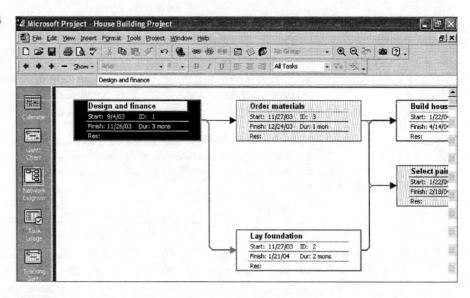

with the problem of having to reduce the scheduled completion time of a project to meet a deadline. In other words, the manager must finish the project sooner than indicated by the CPM or PERT network analysis.

Project duration can be reduced by assigning more labor to project activities, often in the form of overtime, and by assigning more resources (material, equipment, etc.). However, additional labor and resources cost money and hence increase the overall project cost. Thus, the decision to reduce the project duration must be based on an analysis of the *trade-off* between time and cost.

Project crashing *shortens the project time by reducing critical activity times at a cost.*

Project crashing is a method for shortening the project duration by reducing the time of one or more of the critical project activities to a time that is less than the normal activity time. This reduction in the normal activity times is referred to as *crashing*. Crashing is achieved by devoting more resources, measured in terms of dollars, to the activities to be crashed.

To demonstrate how project crashing works, we will employ the network for constructing a house first introduced in Figure 2. This network is repeated in Figure 19, except that the activity times previously shown as months have been converted to weeks. Although this example network encompasses only single-activity time estimates, the project crashing procedure can be applied in the same manner to PERT networks with probabilistic activity time estimates.

Figure 19

Network for constructing a house

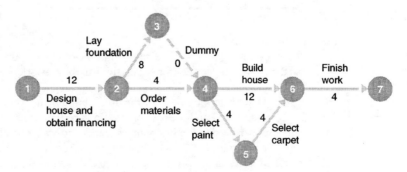

In Figure 19, we will assume that the times (in weeks) shown on the network activities are the *normal activity times*. For example, normally 12 weeks are required to complete activity 1 → 2. Furthermore, we will assume that the cost required to complete this activity in the time indicated is $3,000. This cost is referred to as the *normal activity cost*. Next, we will assume that the building contractor has estimated that activity 1 → 2 can be completed in seven weeks, but it will cost $5,000 to complete the activity instead of $3,000. This new estimated activity time is known as the *crash time*, and the revised cost is referred to as the *crash cost*.

Activity 1 → 2 can be crashed at a total of five weeks (normal time − crash time = 12 − 7 = 5 weeks) at a total crash cost of $2,000 (crash cost − normal cost = $5,000 − 3,000 = $2,000). Dividing the total crash cost by the total allowable crash time yields the crash cost per week.

$$\frac{\text{total crash cost}}{\text{total crash time}} = \frac{\$2,000}{5} = \$400 \text{ per week}$$

Crash cost and crash time have a linear relationship.

If we assume that the relationship between crash cost and crash time is linear, then activity 1 → 2 can be crashed by any amount of time (not exceeding the maximum allowable crash time) at a rate of $400 per week. For example, if the contractor decided to crash activity 1 → 2 by only 2 weeks (for an activity time of 10 weeks), the crash cost would be $800 ($400 per week × 2 weeks). The linear relationships between crash cost and crash time and between normal cost and normal time are illustrated in Figure 20.

Figure 20

Time–cost relationship for crashing activity 1 → 2

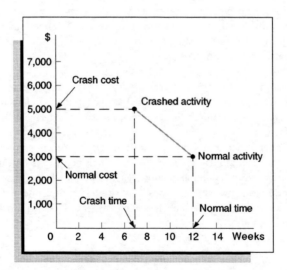

The normal times and costs, the crash times and costs, the total allowable crash times, and the crash cost per week for each activity in the network in Figure 19 are summarized in Table 5.

Recall that the critical path for the house-building network encompassed activities 1 → 2 → 3 → 4 → 6 → 7 and the project duration was 9 months, or 36 weeks. Suppose that the home builder needed the house in 30 weeks and wanted to know how much extra cost would be incurred to complete the house by this time. To analyze this situation, the contractor would crash the project network to 30 weeks using the information in Table 5.

Table 5

Normal activity and crash data for the network in Figure 19

Activity	Normal Time (weeks)	Crash Time (weeks)	Normal Cost	Crash Cost	Total Allowable Crash Time (weeks)	Crash Cost per Week
1 → 2	12	7	$3,000	$5,000	5	$400
2 → 3	8	5	2,000	3,500	3	500
2 → 4	4	3	4,000	7,000	1	3,000
3 → 4	0	0	0	0	0	0
4 → 5	4	1	500	1,100	3	200
4 → 6	12	9	50,000	71,000	3	7,000
5 → 6	4	1	500	1,100	3	200
6 → 7	4	3	15,000	22,000	1	7,000
			$75,000	$110,700		

As activities are crashed, the critical path may change and several paths may become critical.

The objective of project crashing is to reduce the project duration while minimizing the cost of crashing. Since the project completion time can be shortened only by crashing activities on the critical path, it may turn out that not all activities have to be crashed. However, as activities are crashed, the critical path may change, requiring crashing of previously noncritical activities to further reduce the project completion time.

We start the crashing process by looking at the critical path and seeing which activity has the minimum crash cost per week. Observing Table 5 and Figure 21, we see that activity 1 → 2 has the minimum crash cost of $400 (excluding the dummy activity 3 → 4, which cannot be reduced). Thus, activity 1 → 2 will be reduced as much as possible. Table 5 shows that the maximum allowable reduction for activity 1 → 2 is five weeks, *but we can reduce activity 1 → 2 only to the point where another path becomes critical.* When two paths simultaneously become critical, activities on both must be reduced by the same amount. (If we reduce the activity time beyond the point where another path becomes critical, we may be incurring an unnecessary cost.) This last stipulation means that we must keep up with all of the network paths as we reduce individual activities, a condition that makes manual crashing very cumbersome. Later we will demonstrate an alternative method for project crashing using linear programming; however, for the moment we will pursue this example in order to demonstrate the logic of project crashing.

Figure 21

Network with normal activity times and weekly activity crashing costs

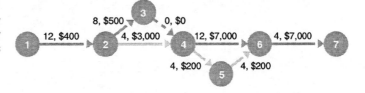

It turns out that activity 1 → 2 can be crashed by the total amount of five weeks without another path's becoming critical, because activity 1 → 2 is included in all four paths in the network. Crashing this activity results in a revised project duration of 31 weeks at a crashing cost of $2,000. The revised network is shown in Figure 22.

Figure 22

The revised network with activity 1 → 2 crashed

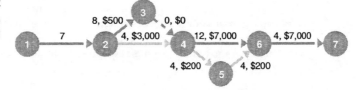

This process must now be repeated. The critical path in Figure 22 remains the same, and the minimum activity crash cost on the critical path is $500 for activity 2 → 3. Activity 2 → 3 can be crashed a total of 3 weeks, but because the contractor desires to crash the network to only 30 weeks, we need to crash activity 2 → 3 by only 1 week. Crashing activity 1 → 2 by 1 week does not result in any other path's becoming critical, so we can safely make this reduction. Crashing activity 2 → 3 to 7 weeks (i.e., a one-week reduction) costs $500 and reduces the project duration to 30 weeks.

The extra cost of crashing the project to 30 weeks is $2,500. Thus, the contractor could inform the customer that an additional cost of only $2,500 would be incurred to finish the house in 30 weeks.

As indicated earlier, the manual procedure for crashing a network is very cumbersome and generally unacceptable for project crashing. It is basically a trial-and-error approach that is useful for demonstrating the logic of crashing; however, it quickly becomes unmanageable for larger networks. This approach would have become difficult if we had pursued even the house-building example to a crash time greater than 30 weeks.

Project Crashing with QM for Windows

QM for Windows also has the capability to crash a network *completely*. In other words, it crashes the network by the maximum amount possible. In our house-building example in the previous section we crashed the network to only 30 weeks, and we did not consider by how much the network could have actually been crashed. Alternatively, QM for Windows crashes the network by the maximum amount possible. The QM for Windows solution for our house-building example is shown in Exhibit 6. Notice that the network has been crashed to 24 weeks at a total crash cost of $31,500.

Exhibit 6

Project Management (PERT/CPM) Results

House Building Example Solution								
	Start node	End node	Normal time	Crash time	Normal Cost	Crash Cost	Crash cost/pd	Crash by	Crashing cost
Project			36.	24.					
Design house	1.	2.	12.	7.	3,000.	5,000.	400.	5.	2,000.
Lay foundation	2.	3.	8.	5.	2,000.	3,500.	500.	3.	1,500.
Order materials	2.	4.	4.	3.	4,000.	7,000.	3,000.	0.	0.
Dummy	3.	4.	0.	0.	0.	0.	0.	0.	0.
Select paint	4.	5.	4.	1.	500.	1,100.	200.	0.	0.
Build house	4.	6.	12.	9.	50,000.	71,000.	7,000.	3.	21,000.
Select carpet	5.	6.	4.	1.	500.	1,100.	200.	0.	0.
Finish work	6.	7.	4.	3.	15,000.	22,000.	7,000.	1.	7,000.
TOTALS					75,000.				31,500.

The General Relationship of Time and Cost

In our discussion of project crashing, we demonstrated how the project critical path time could be reduced by increasing expenditures for labor and direct resources. The implicit objective of crashing was to reduce the scheduled completion time for its own sake—that is, to reap the results of the project sooner. However, there may be other important reasons for reducing project time. As projects continue over time, they consume various *indirect costs*, including the cost of facilities, equipment, and machinery; interest on investment;

Management Science Application

Kodak's Advantix *Advanced Photo System Project*

On April 22, 1996, consumers around the world were able to purchase products and services from an entirely new photographic system developed by Kodak: the *Advantix* Advanced Photo System (APS). This new system included a film cassette that could be easily loaded into a camera without the need to thread the film, and a film format 60% the size of the traditional 35mm film negative allowing for smaller, more portable cameras. It also enabled a user to select from any of three print sizes when taking a photo, it returned processed negatives in their original cassette, and it included an index print with a miniature image of each picture in the set—camera features that are now commonplace. This photographic system project, nicknamed "Orion," was the most complicated ever undertaken by Kodak. Whereas most photographic system projects at Kodak invoke only a single element, this project required changes in all components. The film base for color negative film had changed only twice in Kodak's 115-year history, but this project altered not only the film base but also the film packaging, the cameras, and the photo finishing equipment.

Kodak wanted to develop one worldwide industry standard and minimize the risk of competing standards that would only confuse the industry and consumers so it reached an agreement with three leading camera companies, Canon, Minolta, and Nikon, as well as its top film competitor, Fuji, to initiate project Orion. (Licenses were subsequently offered to other photographic companies so they could also make products or offer services for the APS.)

The five partnered companies created a series of interlocking global teams and committees to set overall strategy, to evaluate and recommend key features and technologies, to define the detailed key dimensions and protocols, and to transfer knowledge about the system to the industry through licensing agreements. Faxes and e-mail communication were essential in daily communication among the companies, as well as an in-person meeting

Photo courtesy of PhotoEdit

every six weeks. One team leader logged over one million flying miles over five years between Rochester, New York, and Japan.

Kodak established its own formal project management team in early 1992. It included approximately 1,000 employees dedicated full-time to the project, and another 7,000 employees received security clearance to work on the project at various times. Special attention was given to project security and no information was given to other Kodak employees until the new system was introduced. The project team managed the project via 300 key project milestones established using project software, primarily Microsoft Project. Progress against milestones in each area was reported monthly at scheduled meetings. Each area filed a one- to two-page report that included accomplishments, concerns, and plans. When the new system was formally announced to the public in February 1996 Kodak had invested $500 million in the project and expected to spend another $500 million before the success of the system could be fully measured.

Source: C. Adams, "A Kodak Moment: *Advantix* Project Named 1997 International Project of the Year," *PM Network* 12, no. 1, (January 1998): 21–27.

Crashing costs increase as project time decreases; indirect costs increase as project time increases.

utilities, labor, and personnel costs; and the loss of skills and labor from members of the project team who are not working at their regular jobs. There also may be direct financial penalties for not completing a project on time. For example, many construction contracts and government contracts have penalty clauses for exceeding the project completion date.

In general, project crashing costs and indirect costs have an inverse relationship; crashing costs are highest when the project is shortened, whereas indirect costs increase as the project duration increases. This time–cost relationship is illustrated in Figure 23. The best or optimal project time is at the minimum point on the total cost curve.

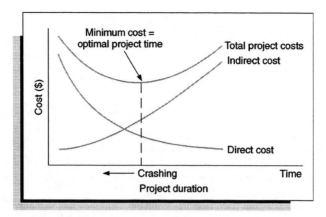

Figure 23

The time–cost trade-off

Formulating the CPM/PERT Network as a Linear Programming Model

First we will look at the linear programming formulation of the general CPM/PERT network model, and then the formulation of the project crashing network.

As the first step in formulating the linear programming model, we will define the decision variables. In our general discussion of CPM/PERT networks, we designated an activity by its starting and ending node numbers. Thus, an activity starting at node 1 and ending at node 2 was referred to as activity $1 \rightarrow 2$. We will use a similar designation to define the decision variables of our linear programming model.

The objective function for the linear programming model is to minimize project duration.

We will also use a different scheduling convention. Instead of determining the earliest activity start time for each activity, we will use the *earliest event time* at each node. This is the earliest time that a node (i or j) can be realized. In other words, it is the earliest time that the event the node represents, either the completion of all the activities leading into it or the start of all activities leaving it, can occur. Thus, for an activity $i \rightarrow j$, the earliest event time of node i will be x_i, and the earliest event time of node j will be x_j.

The objective of the project network is to determine the earliest time the project can be completed (i.e., the critical path time). We have already determined from our discussion of CPM/PERT network analysis that the earliest event time of the last node in the network equals the critical path time. If we let x_i equal the earliest event times of the nodes in the network, then the objective function can be expressed as

$$\text{minimize } Z = \sum_i x_i$$

Because the value of Z is the sum of all the earliest event times it has no real meaning; however, it will ensure the earliest event time at each node.

Next, we must develop the model constraints. We will define the time for activity $i \rightarrow j$ as t_{ij} (as we did earlier in this chapter). From our previous discussion of CPM/PERT network analysis, we know that the difference between the earliest event time at node j and the earliest event time at node i must be at least as great as the activity time t_{ij}. A set of constraints that expresses this condition is defined as

$$x_j - x_i \geq t_{ij}$$

The general linear programming model of formulation of a CPM/PERT network can be summarized as

$$\text{minimize } Z = \sum_i x_i$$

subject to
$$x_j - x_i \geq t_{ij}, \text{ for all activities } i \rightarrow j$$
$$x_i, x_j \geq 0$$

where

x_i = earliest event time of node i
x_j = earliest event time of node j
t_{ij} = time of activity $i \rightarrow j$

The solution of this linear programming model will indicate the earliest event time of each node in the network and the project duration.

As an example of the linear programming model formulation and solution of a project network, we will use our house-building network that we used to demonstrate project crashing. This network, with activity times in weeks and earliest event times, is shown in Figure 24.

Figure 24

CPM/PERT network for the house-building project with earliest event times

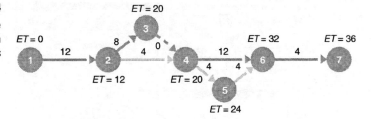

The linear programming model for the network in Figure 24 is

$$\text{minimize } Z = x_1 + x_2 + x_3 + x_4 + x_5 + x_6 + x_7$$
subject to
$$x_2 - x_1 \geq 12$$
$$x_3 - x_2 \geq 8$$
$$x_4 - x_2 \geq 4$$
$$x_4 - x_3 \geq 0$$
$$x_5 - x_4 \geq 4$$
$$x_6 - x_4 \geq 12$$
$$x_6 - x_5 \geq 4$$
$$x_7 - x_6 \geq 4$$
$$x_i, x_j \geq 0$$

Notice in this model that there is a constraint for every activity in the network.

Solution of the CPM/PERT Linear Programming Model with Excel

The linear programming model of the CPM/PERT network in the preceding section enables us to use Excel to schedule the project. Exhibit 7 shows an Excel spreadsheet set up to determine the earliest event times for each node, that is, the x_i and x_j values in our linear programming model for our house-building example. The earliest start times are in cells **B6:B12**. Cells **F6:F13** contain the model constraints. For example, cell F6 contains the constraint formula "**=B7–B6**" and cell F7 contains the formula "**=B8–B7**." These constraint formulas will be set $\geq$ to the activity times in column G when we access the "Solver." (Also, because activity $3 \rightarrow 4$ is a dummy, a constraint for **F9=0** must be added to the "Solver.")

Exhibit 7

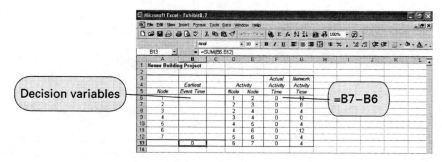

The "Solver" is accessed from the "Tools" menu located at the top of the spreadsheet. The "Solver" with the model data is shown in Exhibit 8. Notice that the objective is to minimize the project duration in cell B13, which actually contains the earliest event time for node 7.

Exhibit 8

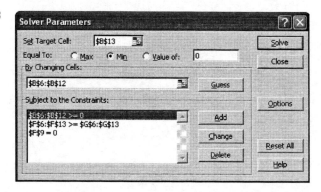

The solution is shown in Exhibit 9. Notice that the earliest time at each node is given in cells **B6:B12** and the total project duration is 36 weeks. However, this output does not indicate the critical path. The critical path can be determined by accessing the "Sensitivity Report" for this problem. Recall that when you click on "Solve" from the "Solver," a screen

Exhibit 9

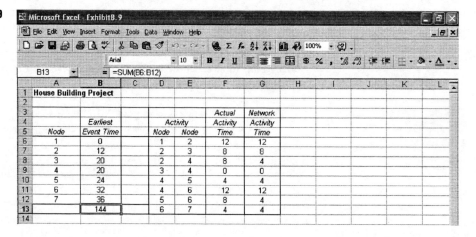

comes up indicating that "Solver" has reached a solution. This screen also provides the opportunity to generate several different kinds of reports, including an "Answer Report" and a "Sensitivity Report." By clicking on "Sensitivity" under the report options, the information shown in Exhibit 10 is provided.

Exhibit 10

Constraints						
Cell	Name	Final Value	Shadow Price	Constraint R.H. Side	Allowable Increase	Allowable Decrease
F6	Time	12	1	12	1E+30	12
F7	Time	8	1	8	1E+30	4
F8	Time	8	0	4	4	1E+30
F9	Time	0	1	0	1E+30	4
F10	Time	8	0	4	4	1E+30
F11	Time	12	1	12	1E+30	4
F12	Time	4	0	4	4	1E+30
F13	weeks Time	4	1	4	1E+30	36

Indicates critical path

The information in which we are interested is the shadow price for each of the activity constraints. (Remember that to get the shadow prices on the sensitivity report you must click on "Options" from the "Solver" and then select "Assume Linear Model." The shadow price for each activity will be either 1 or 0. A positive shadow price of 1 for an activity means that you can reduce the overall project duration by an amount with a corresponding decrease by the same amount in the activity duration. Alternatively, a shadow price of 0 means that the project duration will not change even if you change the activity duration by some amount. This means that those activities with a shadow price of 1 are on the critical path. Cells F6, F7, F9, F11, and F13 have shadow prices of 1, and referring back to Exhibit 9 we see that these cells correspond to activities 1–2, 2–3, 3–4, 4–6, and 6–7, which are the activities on the critical path.

Project Crashing with Linear Programming

The objective of the project crashing model is to minimize the cost of crashing.

The linear programming model required to perform project crashing analysis differs from the linear programming model formulated for the general CPM/PERT network in the previous section. The linear programming model for project crashing is somewhat longer and more complex.

The objective for our general linear programming model was to minimize project duration; the objective of project crashing is to minimize the cost of crashing given the limits on how much individual activities can be crashed. As a result, the general linear programming model formulation must be expanded to include crash times and cost. We will continue to define the earliest event times for activity $i \rightarrow j$ as x_i and x_j. In addition, we will define the amount of time each activity $i \rightarrow j$ is crashed as y_{ij}. Thus, the decision variables are defined as

x_i = earliest event time of node i
x_j = earliest event time of node j
y_{ij} = amount of time by which activity $i \rightarrow j$ is crashed (i.e., reduced)

The objective of project crashing is to reduce the project duration at the minimum possible crash cost. For our house-building network, the objective function is written as

minimize $Z = \$400y_{12} + 500y_{23} + 3,000y_{24} + 200y_{45} + 7,000y_{46} + 200y_{56} + 200y_{56} + 7,000y_{67}$

The objective function coefficients are the activity crash costs per week from Table 5; the variables y_{ij} indicate the number of weeks each activity will be reduced. For example, if activity $1 \rightarrow 2$ is crashed by 2 weeks, then $y_{12} = 2$ and a cost of \$800 is incurred.

The model constraints must specify the limits on the amount of time each activity can be crashed. Using the allowable crash times for each activity from Table 5 enables us to develop the following set of constraints.

$$y_{12} \leq 5$$
$$y_{23} \leq 3$$
$$y_{24} \leq 1$$
$$y_{34} \leq 0$$
$$y_{45} \leq 3$$
$$y_{46} \leq 3$$
$$y_{56} \leq 3$$
$$y_{67} \leq 1$$

For example, the first constraint, $y_{12} \leq 5$, specifies that the amount of time that activity $1 \rightarrow 2$ is reduced cannot exceed five weeks.

The next group of constraints must mathematically represent the relationship between earliest event times for each activity in the network, as the constraint $x_j - x_i \geq t_{ij}$ did in our original linear programming model. However, we must now reflect the fact that activity times can be crashed by an amount y_{ij}. Recall the formulation of the activity $1 \rightarrow 2$ constraint for the general linear programming model formulation in the previous section:

$$x_2 - x_1 \geq 12$$

This constraint can also be written as

$$x_1 + 12 \leq x_2$$

This latter constraint indicates that the earliest event time at node 1 (x_1) plus the normal activity time (12 weeks) cannot exceed the earliest event time at node 2 (x_2). To reflect the fact that this activity can be crashed, it is necessary only to subtract the amount by which it can be crashed from the left-hand side of the preceding constraint.

amount activity $1 \rightarrow 2$ can be crashed

$$x_1 + 12 - y_{12} \leq x_2$$

This revised constraint now indicates that the earliest event time at node 2 (x_2) is determined not only by the earliest event time at node 1 plus the activity time, but also by the amount the activity is crashed. Each activity in the network must have a similar constraint, as follows.

$$x_1 + 12 - y_{12} \leq x_2$$
$$x_2 + 8 - y_{23} \leq x_3$$
$$x_2 + 4 - y_{24} \leq x_4$$
$$x_3 + 0 - y_{34} \leq x_4$$
$$x_4 + 4 - y_{45} \leq x_5$$
$$x_4 + 12 - y_{46} \leq x_6$$
$$x_5 + 4 - y_{56} \leq x_6$$
$$x_6 + 4 - y_{67} \leq x_7$$

Finally, we must indicate the project duration we are seeking (i.e., the crashed project time). Because the housing contractor wants to crash the project from the 36-week normal critical path time to 30 weeks, our final model constraint specifies that the earliest event time at node 7 should not exceed 30 weeks:

$$x_7 \leq 30$$

The complete linear programming model formulation is summarized as follows.

minimize $Z = \$400y_{12} + 500y_{23} + 3{,}000y_{24} + 200y_{45} + 7{,}000y_{46} + 200y_{56} + 7{,}000y_{67}$
subject to

$$y_{12} \leq 5$$
$$y_{23} \leq 3$$
$$y_{24} \leq 1$$
$$y_{34} \leq 0$$
$$y_{45} \leq 3$$
$$y_{46} \leq 3$$
$$y_{56} \leq 3$$
$$y_{67} \leq 1$$
$$y_{12} + x_2 - x_1 \geq 12$$
$$y_{23} + x_3 - x_2 \geq 8$$
$$y_{24} + x_4 - x_2 \geq 4$$
$$y_{34} + x_4 - x_3 \geq 0$$
$$y_{45} + x_5 - x_4 \geq 4$$
$$y_{46} + x_6 - x_4 \geq 12$$
$$y_{56} + x_6 - x_5 \geq 4$$
$$x_{67} + x_7 - x_6 \geq 4$$
$$x_7 \leq 30$$
$$x_i, y_{ij} \geq 0$$

Project Crashing with Excel

Because we have been able to develop a linear programming model for project crashing, we can also solve this model using Excel. Exhibit 11 shows a modified version of the Excel spreadsheet we developed earlier in Exhibit 7 to determine the earliest event times for our CPM/PERT network for the house-building project. We have added columns H, I, and J for

Exhibit 11

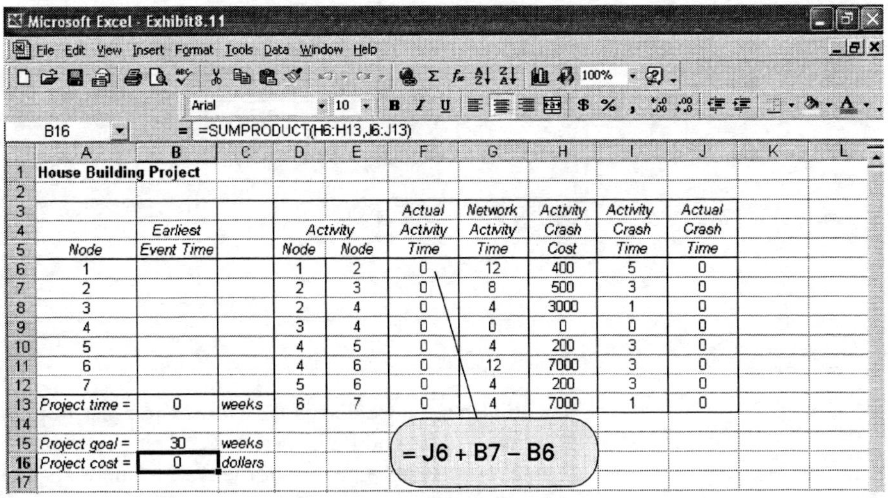

the activity crash costs, the activity crash times, and the actual activity crash times. Cells **J6:J13** correspond to the y_{ij} variables in the linear programming model. The constraint formulas for each activity are included in cells **F6:F13**. For example, cell F6 contains the formula "=J6+B7−B6" and cell F7 contains the formula "=J7+B8−B7." These constraints and the others in column F must be set $\geq$ to the activity times in column G. The objective function formula in cell B16 is shown on the formula bar at the top of the spreadsheet. The crashing goal of 30 weeks is included in cell B15.

The problem in Exhibit 11 is solved using the "Solver" shown in Exhibit 12. Notice that there are two sets of variables in cells **B6:B12** and **J6:J13**. The project crashing solution is shown in Exhibit 13.

Exhibit 12

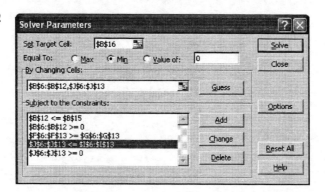

Exhibit 13

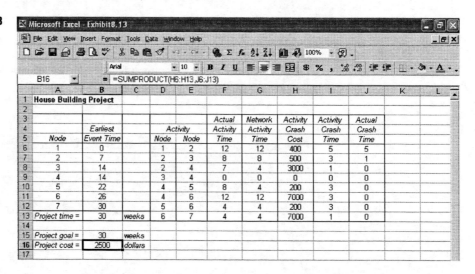

Summary

In this chapter we discussed two of the most popular management science techniques—CPM and PERT networks. Their popularity is due primarily to the fact that a network forms a picture of the system under analysis that is easy for a manager to interpret. Sometimes it is difficult to explain a set of mathematical equations to a manager, but a network often can be easily explained. CPM/PERT has been applied in a variety of government agencies concerned with project control, including various military agencies, NASA, the Federal Aviation Agency (FAA), and the General Services Administration (GSA). These agencies are frequently involved in large-scale projects involving millions of dollars and many subcontractors. Examples of such governmental projects include the development of weapons systems, aircraft, and such NASA space exploration projects as the Space Shuttle. It has become a common practice for these agencies to require subcontractors to develop and use a CPM/PERT analysis to maintain management control of the myriad of project components and subprojects.

CPM/PERT has also been widely applied in the private sector. Two of the major areas of application of CPM/PERT in the private sector have been research and development and construction. CPM/PERT has been applied to various R&D projects, such as developing new drugs, planning and introducing new products, and developing new and more powerful computer systems. CPM/PERT analysis has been particularly applicable to construction projects. Almost every type of construction project—from building a house to constructing a major sports stadium to building a ship to constructing the Alaska oil pipeline—has been subjected to network analysis.

Network analysis is also applicable to the planning and scheduling of major events, such as summit conferences, sports festivals, basketball tournaments, football bowl games, parades, political conventions, school registrations, or rock concerts. The availability of powerful, user-friendly project management software packages for the personal computer will serve only to increase the use of this technique.

References

Levy, F., Thompson, G., and Wiest, J. "The ABC's of the Critical Path Method." *Harvard Business Review* 41, no. 5 (October 1963).

Moder, J., Phillips, C. R., and Davis, E. W. *Project Management with CPM and PERT and Precedence Diagramming.* 3rd ed. New York: Van Nostrand Reinhold, 1983.

O'Brian, J. *CPM in Construction Management.* New York: McGraw-Hill, 1965.

Wiest, J. D., and Levy, F. K. *A Management Guide to PERT/CPM.* 2nd ed. Englewood Cliffs, N.J.: Prentice-Hall, 1977.

Example Problem Solution

The following example will illustrate PERT network analysis and probability analysis.

Problem Statement

Given the following network and PERT activity time estimates, determine the expected project completion time and variance, and the probability that the project will be completed in 28 days or less.

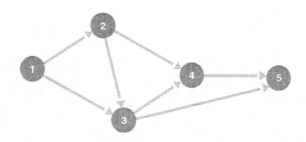

Activity	Time Estimates (weeks)		
	a	m	b
1 → 2	5	8	17
1 → 3	7	10	13
2 → 3	3	5	7
2 → 4	1	3	5
3 → 4	4	6	8
3 → 5	3	3	3
4 → 5	3	4	5

Solution

Step 1: Compute the Expected Activity Times and Variances

Using the following formulas, compute the expected time and variance for each activity.

$$t = \frac{a + 4m + b}{6}$$

$$v = \left(\frac{b - a}{6}\right)^2$$

For example, the expected time and variance for activity 1 → 2 are

$$t = \frac{5 + 4(8) + 17}{6}$$

$$= 9$$

$$v = \left(\frac{17 - 5}{6}\right)^2$$

$$= 4$$

These values and the remaining expected times and variances for each activity follow.

Activity	t	v
1 → 2	9	4
1 → 3	10	1
2 → 3	5	4/9
2 → 4	3	4/9
3 → 4	6	4/9
3 → 5	3	0
4 → 5	4	1/9

Step 2: Determine the Earliest and Latest Times at Each Node

The earliest and latest activity times and the activity slack are shown on the following network.

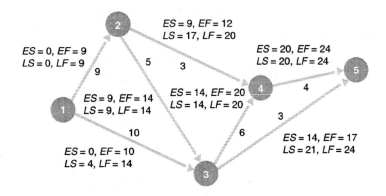

Step 3: Identify the Critical Path and Compute Expected Project Completion Time and Variance

Observing the foregoing network and those activities with no slack (i.e., $S = 0$), we can identify the critical path as $1 \rightarrow 2 \rightarrow 3 \rightarrow 4 \rightarrow 5$. The expected project completion time (t_P) is 24 days. The variance is computed by summing the variances for the activities in the critical path:

$$v_p = 4 + 4/9 + 4/9 + 1/9$$
$$= 5 \text{ days}$$

Step 4: Determine the Probability That the Project Will Be Completed in 28 Days or Less

The following normal probability distribution describes the probability analysis.

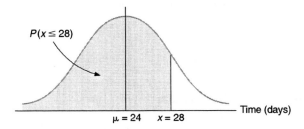

Compute Z using the following formula.

$$Z = \frac{x - \mu}{\sigma}$$
$$= \frac{28 - 24}{\sqrt{5}}$$
$$= 1.79$$

The corresponding probability from the table of "Normal Curve Areas" is .4633; thus,

$$P(x \leq 28) = .9633$$

1. Construct the CPM network described by the following set of activities, compute the length of each path in the network, and indicate the critical path.

Activity	Time (weeks)
1 → 2	5
1 → 3	4
2 → 4	3
3 → 4	6

2. Construct the CPM network described by the following set of activities, compute the length of each path in the network, and indicate the critical path.

Activity	Time (weeks)
1 → 2	3
1 → 3	7
2 → 4	2
3 → 4	5
3 → 5	6
4 → 6	1
5 → 6	4

3. Construct the CPM network described by the following set of activities, compute the length of each path in the network, and indicate the critical path.

Activity	Time (months)
1 → 2	4
1 → 3	7
2 → 4	8
2 → 5	3
3 → 5	9
4 → 5	5
4 → 6	2
5 → 6	6
3 → 6	5

4. Identify all of the paths in the following network, compute the length of each, and indicate the critical path. (Activity times are in weeks.)

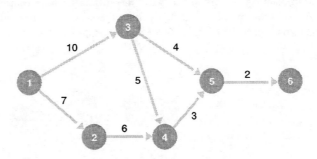

5. For the network in problem 4, determine the earliest and latest activity times and slack for each activity. Indicate how the critical path would be determined from this information.

6. Given the following network with activity times in months, determine the earliest and latest activity times and slack for each activity. Indicate the critical path and the project duration.

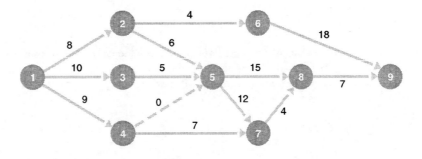

7. Given the following network with activity times in weeks, determine the earliest and latest activity times and slack for each activity. Indicate the critical path and the project duration.

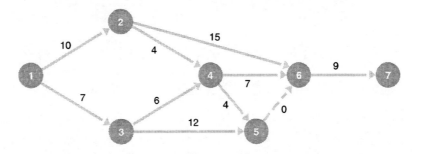

8. In one of the little-known battles of the Civil War, General Tecumseh Beauregard lost the Third Battle of Bull Run because his preparations were not complete when the enemy attacked. If the critical path method had been available, the general could have planned better. Suppose that the following planning network with activity times in days had been available. Determine the earliest and latest activity times, and activity slack for the network. Indicate the critical path and the time between the general's receipt of battle orders and the onset of battle.

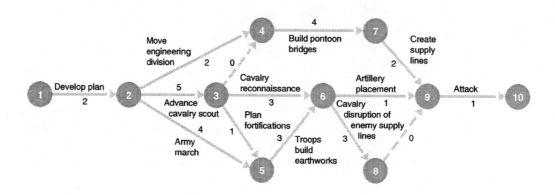

9. A group of developers is building a new shopping center. A consultant for the developers has constructed the following project network and assigned activity times in weeks. Determine the earliest and latest activity times, activity slack, critical path, and duration for the project.

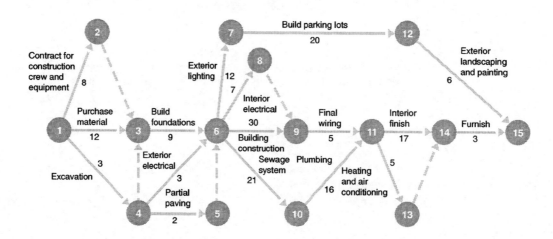

10. A farm owner is going to erect a maintenance building with a connecting electrical generator and water tank. The activities, activity descriptions, and estimated durations are given in the following table. (Notice that the activities are defined not by node numbers but by activity descriptions. This

PROJECT MANAGEMENT

alternative form of expressing activities and precedence relationships is often used in CPM/PERT.) Construct the network for this project, identify the critical path, and determine the project duration time.

Activity	Activity Description	Activity Predecessor	Activity Duration (weeks)
a	Excavate	—	2
b	Erect building	a	6
c	Install generator	a	4
d	Install tank	a	2
e	Install maintenance equipment	b	4
f	Connect generator and tank to building	b, c, d	5
g	Paint finish	b	3
h	Check out facility	e, f	2

11. Given the following network and activity time estimates, determine the expected time and variance for each activity, and indicate the critical path.

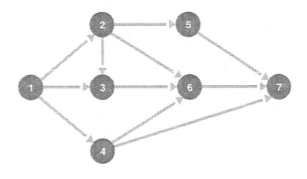

	Time Estimates (weeks)		
Activity	a	m	b
1 → 2	6	10	15
1 → 3	2	7	16
1 → 4	4	8	11
2 → 3	3	10	15
2 → 5	7	9	20
2 → 6	4	12	15
3 → 6	3	6	9
4 → 6	5	9	16
5 → 7	3	20	35
4 → 7	4	12	16
6 → 7	2	9	14

12. The Farmer's American Bank of Leesburg is planning to install a new computerized accounts system. Bank management has determined the activities required to complete the project, the precedence relationships of the activities, and activity time estimates, as shown in the following table. Determine the expected project completion time and variance, and determine the probability that the project will be completed in 40 weeks or less.

Activity	Activity Description	Activity Predecessor	Time Estimates (weeks)		
			a	m	b
a	Position recruiting	—	5	8	17
b	System development	—	3	12	15
c	System training	a	4	7	10
d	Equipment training	a	5	8	23
e	Manual system test	b, c	1	1	1
f	Preliminary system changeover	b, c	1	4	13
g	Computer–personnel interface	d, e	3	6	9
h	Equipment modification	d, e	1	2.5	7
i	Equipment testing	h	1	1	1
j	System debugging and installation	f, g	2	2	2
k	Equipment changeover	g, i	5	8	11

13. The following activity time estimates are for the network in problem 6.

Activity	Time Estimates (months)		
	a	m	b
1 → 2	4	8	12
1 → 3	6	10	15
1 → 4	2	10	14
2 → 5	3	6	9
2 → 6	1	4	13
3 → 5	3	6	18
4 → 5	0	0	0
4 → 7	2	8	12
5 → 8	9	15	22
5 → 7	5	12	21
7 → 8	5	6	12
6 → 9	7	20	25
8 → 9	3	8	20

Determine the following.
   a. Expected activity times
   b. Earliest activity times
   c. Latest activity times
   d. Activity slack
   e. Critical path
   f. Expected project duration and variance

14. The following activity time estimates are for the network in problem 8.

Activity	Time Estimates (days)		
	a	m	b
1 → 2	1	2	6
2 → 4	1	3	5
2 → 3	3	5	10
2 → 5	3	6	14
3 → 4	0	0	0
3 → 5	1	1.5	2
3 → 6	2	3	7
4 → 7	2	4	9
5 → 6	1	3	5
7 → 9	1	2	3
6 → 9	1	1	5
6 → 8	2	4	9
8 → 9	0	0	0
9 → 10	1	1	1

Determine the following.
   a. Expected activity times
   b. Earliest activity times
   c. Latest activity times
   d. Activity slack
   e. Critical path
   f. Expected project duration and variance

15. For the PERT network in problem 13, determine the probability that the network duration will exceed 50 months.

16. The Center for Information Technology at State University has outgrown its office in Bates (B) Hall and is moving to Allen (A) Hall, which has more space. The move will take place during the three week break between the end of summer semester and the beginning of fall semester. Movers will be hired from the university's physical plant to move the furniture, boxes of books, and files that the faculty will pack. The center has hired a local retail computer firm to move its office computers so they won't be damaged. Following is a list of activities, their precedence relationships, and probabilistic time estimates for this project.

Activity	Activity Description	Activity Predecessor	Time Estimates (days)		
			a	m	b
a	Pack "A" offices	—	1	3	5
b	Network "A" offices	—	2	3	5
c	Pack "B" offices	—	2	4	7
d	Movers move "A" offices	a	1	3	4
e	Paint and clean "A" offices	d	2	5	8
f	Move computers	b, e	1	2	2
g	Movers move "B" offices	b, c, e	3	6	8
h	Computer installation	f	2	4	5
i	Faculty move and unpack	g	3	4	6
j	Faculty set up computers and offices	h, i	1	2	4

Determine the earliest and latest start and finish times, the critical path, and the expected project duration. What is the probability the center will complete its move before the start of the fall semester?

17. Jane and Jim Smith are going to give a dinner party on Friday evening at 7:00 P.M. Their two children, Jerry and Judy, are going to help them get ready. The Smiths will all get home from work and school at 4:00 P.M. Jane and Jim have developed a project network to help them schedule their dinner preparations. Following is a list of the activities, the precedence relationships, and activity times involved in the project.

Activity	Activity Description	Activity Predecessor	Time Estimates (mins)		
			a	m	b
a	Prepare salad	—	18	25	31
b	Prepare appetizer	—	15	23	30
c	Dust/clean	—	25	40	56
d	Vacuum	c	20	30	45
e	Prepare dessert	a, b	12	21	30
f	Set table	d	10	17	25
g	Get ice from market	f	5	12	18
h	Prepare/start tenderloin	e	10	20	25
i	Cut and prepare vegetables	e	9	15	22
j	Jim shower and dress	g	8	10	15
k	Jane shower and dress	h, i, j	20	27	40
l	Uncork wine/water carafes	h, i, j	6	10	15
m	Prepare bread	k, l	4	7	10
n	Prepare and set out dishes	k, l	10	14	20
o	Cut meat	k, l	7	15	20
p	Heat vegetable dish	k, l	3	4	6
q	Put out appetizers	m	4	6	7
r	Pour champagne	o	5	8	10

Develop a project network and determine the earliest and latest start and finish times, activity slack, and critical path. Compute the probability that they will be ready by 7:00 P.M.

18. The Stone River Textile Mill was inspected by OSHA and found to be in violation of a number of safety regulations. The OSHA inspectors ordered the mill to alter some existing machinery to make it safer (add safety guards, etc.); purchase some new machinery to replace older, dangerous machinery; and relocate some machinery to make safer passages and unobstructed entrances and exits. OSHA gave the mill only 35 weeks to make the changes; if the changes were not made by then, the mill would be fined $300,000.

The mill determined the activities in a CPM/PERT network that would have to be completed and then estimated the indicated activity times, as shown in the following table.

Activity	Activity Description	Activity Predecessor	Time Estimates (weeks)		
			a	m	b
a	Order new machinery	—	1	2	3
b	Plan new physical layout	—	2	5	8
c	Determine safety changes in existing machinery	—	1	3	5
d	Receive equipment	a	4	10	25
e	Hire new employees	a	3	7	12
f	Make plant alterations	b	10	15	25
g	Make changes in existing machinery	c	5	9	14
h	Train new employees	d, e	2	3	7
i	Install new machinery	d, e, f	1	4	6
j	Relocate old machinery	d, e, f, g	2	5	10
k	Conduct employee safety orientation	h, i, j	2	2	2

Construct the project network for this project and determine the following.
   a. Expected activity times
   b. Earliest and latest activity times and activity slack
   c. Critical path
   d. Expected project duration and variance
   e. The probability that the mill will be fined $300,000

19. In the Third Battle of Bull Run, for which a CPM/PERT network was developed in problem 14, General Beauregard would have won if his preparations had been completed in 15 days. What would the probability of General Beauregard's winning the battle have been?

20. On May 21, 1927, Charles Lindbergh landed at Le Bourget Field in Paris, completing his famous transatlantic solo flight. The preparation period prior to his flight was quite hectic and time was very critical because several other famous pilots of the day were also planning transatlantic flights. Once Ryan Aircraft was contacted to build the *Spirit of St. Louis*, it took only a little over 2½ months to construct the plane and fly it to New York for the takeoff. If CPM/PERT had been available to Charles Lindbergh, it no doubt would have been useful in helping him plan this project. Use your imagination and assume that a CPM/PERT network with the following estimated activity times was developed for the flight. Determine the expected project duration and variance and the probability of completing the project in 67 days.

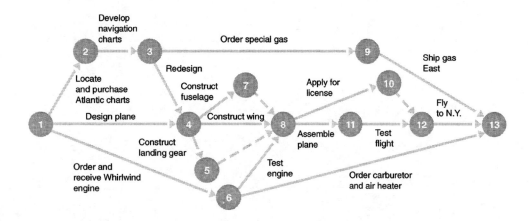

Activity	Time Estimates (days)		
	a	m	b
$1 \rightarrow 2$	1	3	5
$1 \rightarrow 4$	4	6	10
$1 \rightarrow 6$	20	35	50
$2 \rightarrow 3$	4	7	12
$3 \rightarrow 4$	2	3	5
$4 \rightarrow 7$	8	12	25
$4 \rightarrow 8$	10	16	21
$4 \rightarrow 5$	5	9	15
$3 \rightarrow 9$	6	8	14
$6 \rightarrow 8$	1	2	2
$6 \rightarrow 13$	5	8	12
$8 \rightarrow 10$	5	10	15
$8 \rightarrow 11$	4	7	10
$9 \rightarrow 13$	5	7	12
$11 \rightarrow 12$	5	9	20
$12 \rightarrow 13$	1	3	7

21. RusTech Tooling, is a large job shop operation that builds machine tools and dies to manufacture parts for specialized items. The company primarily bids on government-related contracts to produce parts for such items as military aircraft and weapons systems, and the space program. The company is bidding on a contract to produce a component part for the fuselage assembly in a new space shuttle. A major criterion for selecting the winning bid, besides low cost, is the time required to produce the part. However, if the company is awarded the contract it will be strictly held to the completion date specified in the bid, and any delays will result in severe financial penalties. To determine the project completion time to put in its bid, the company has identified the project activities, precedence relationships, and activity times shown in the table below. If RusTech wants to be 90% certain that it can deliver the part without incurring a penalty, what time frame should it specify in the bid?

Activity	Activity Predecessor	Time Estimates (weeks)		
		a	m	b
a	—	3	5	9
b	a	2	5	8
c	a	1	4	6
d	a	4	6	10
e	b	2	8	11
f	b	5	9	16
g	c	4	12	20
h	c	6	9	13
i	d	3	7	14
j	d	8	14	22
k	f, g	9	12	20
l	h, i	6	11	15
m	e	4	7	12
n	j	3	8	16
o	n	5	10	18

22. PM Computers is an international manufacturer of computer equipment and software. It is going to introduce a number of new products in the coming year and it wants to develop marketing programs to accompany the product introductions. The marketing program includes the preparation of printed materials distributed directly by the company and used by the company's marketing personnel, vendors and representatives; print advertising in regular magazines, trade journals, and newspapers; and television commercials. The program also includes extensive training programs for marketing personnel, vendors, and representatives about the new products. A project management team with members from the marketing department and manufacturing areas has developed the following list of activities for the development of the marketing program. Construct the network for this project and determine the activity schedule. Identify the critical path and determine the expected project duration time and variance. What is the probability the program can be completed within four months?

Activity	Activity Description	Activity Predecessor	Time Estimates (days)		
			a	m	b
a	Preliminary budget and plan approval	—	10	15	20
b	Select marketing personnel for training	—	5	9	12
c	Develop overall media plan	a	15	25	30
d	Prepare separate media plans	c	12	20	25
e	Develop training plan	c	5	8	12
f	Design training course	e	6	14	20
g	Train marketing personnel	b, f	16	20	25
h	Plan TV commercials with agency	d	15	25	35
i	Draft in-house print materials	d	8	15	20
j	Develop print advertising layouts with agency	d	16	23	30
k	Review print advertising layouts	j	4	9	12
l	Review TV commercials	h	3	7	12
m	Review and print in-house materials	i	3	5	7
n	Release advertising to print media	g, i, k	2	4	8
o	Release TV commercials to networks	l	4	7	10
p	Final marketing personnel review	g, i, k	4	5	9
q	Run media advertising, mailings	m, n, o	15	20	30

23. The Valley United Soccer Club is planning a soccer tournament for the weekend of April 29 and 30. The club's officers know that by March 30 they must send out acceptances to teams that have applied to enter and that by April 15 they must send out the tournament game schedule to teams that have been selected to play. Their tentative plan is to begin the initial activities for tournament preparation, including sending out the application forms to prospective teams, on January 20. Following is a list of tournament activities, their precedence relationships, and estimates of their duration in days.

Develop a project network for the club's tournament preparation process and determine the likelihood that they will meet their schedule milestones and complete the process according to the scheduled tournament date of April 29.

Activity	Activity Description	Activity Predecessor	Time Estimates (days)		
			a	m	b
a	Send application forms	—	5	7	10
b	Get volunteer workers	—	10	18	26
c	Line up referees	—	7	10	14
d	Reserve fields	—	14	21	35
e	Receive and process forms	a	30	30	30
f	Determine age divisions	b, c, d, e	4	9	12
g	Assign fields to divisions	f	4	7	10
h	Sell program ads	b	14	21	30
i	Acquire donated items for team gift bags	b	15	20	26
j	Schedule games	g	6	14	18
k	Design ads	h	5	8	10
l	Fill gift bags	i	9	12	17
m	Process team T-shirt orders	e	7	10	14
n	Send acceptance letters	f	4	7	12
o	Design and print programs	j, k, l, n	14	18	24
p	Put together registration boxes (programs, gifts, etc.)	o	5	7	10
q	Send out game schedules	j, k, l, n	5	8	12
r	Assign referees to games	j, k, l, n	4	7	10
s	Get trophies	f	20	28	35
t	Silk-screen T-shirts	m	12	17	25
u	Package team T-shirt orders	t	5	8	12

24. During a violent thunderstorm with very high wind gusts in the third week of March, the broadcast tower for the public radio station, WVPR, atop Poor Mountain in Roanoke collapsed. This greatly reduced the strength of the station's signal in the area. The station management immediately began plans to construct a new tower. Following is a list of the required activities for building the new tower with optimistic (a), most likely (m), and pessimistic (b) time estimates (in days). However, the sequence of the activities has not been designated.

Activity	Activity Description	Time Estimates (days)		
		a	m	b
a	Removal of debris	5	8	12
b	Survey new tower site	3	6	8
c	Procure structural steel	15	21	30
d	Procure electrical/broadcasting equipment	18	32	40
e	Grade tower site	4	7	10
f	Pour concrete footings and anchors	10	18	22
g	Delivery and unload steel	3	5	9
h	Delivery and unload electrical/broadcast equipment	1	2	4
i	Erect tower	25	35	50
j	Connect electrical cables between tower and building	4	6	10
k	Construct storm drains and tiles	10	15	21
l	Backfill and grade tower site	4	7	9
m	Clean up	3	6	10
n	Obtain inspection approval	1	4	7

Using your best judgment develop a CPM/PERT network for this project and determine the expected project completion time. Also determine the probability that the station signal will be back at full strength within three months.

25. The following table contains the activities for planning a wedding and the activity time estimates. However, the precedence relationships between activities are not included.

Activity	Activity Description	Time (days)		
		a	m	b
a	Determine date	1	10	15
b	Obtain marriage license	1	5	8
c	Select bridal attendants	3	5	7
d	Order dresses	10	14	21
e	Fit dresses	5	10	12
f	Select groomsmen	1	2	4
g	Order tuxedos	3	5	7
h	Find and rent church	6	14	20
i	Hire florist	3	6	10
j	Develop/print programs	15	22	30
k	Hire photographer	3	10	15
l	Develop guest list	14	25	40
m	Order invitations	7	12	20
n	Address and mail invitations	10	15	25
o	Compile RSVP list	30	45	60
p	Reserve reception hall	3	7	10
q	Hire caterer	2	5	8
r	Determine reception menu	10	12	16
s	Make final order	2	4	7
t	Hire band	10	18	21
u	Decorate reception hall	1	2	3
v	Wedding ceremony	0.5	0.5	0.5
w	Wedding reception	0.5	0.5	0.5

Using your best judgment determine the project network, critical path, and expected project duration. If it is the first of January and a couple is planning a June 1 wedding, what is the probability that it can be done on time?

26. The following table provides the information necessary to construct a project network and project crash data.

Activity	(i, j)	Activity Predecessor	Activity Time (weeks)		Activity Cost ($)	
			Normal	Crash	Normal	Crash
a	(1, 2)	—	20	8	1,000	1,480
b	(1, 4)	—	24	20	1,200	1,400
c	(1, 3)	—	14	7	700	1,190
d	(2, 4)	a	10	6	500	820
e	(3, 4)	c	11	5	550	730

a. Construct the project network.

b. Compute the total allowable crash time per activity and the crash cost per week for each activity.

c. Determine the maximum possible crash time for the network, and manually crash the network the maximum amount.

d. Compute the normal project cost and the cost of the crashed project.

e. Formulate the general linear programming model for this network.

f. Formulate the linear programming crashing model that would crash this network by the maximum amount.

27. The following table provides the information necessary to construct a project network and project crash data.

Activity	(i, j)	Activity Predecessor	Activity Time (weeks)		Activity Cost ($)	
			Normal	Crash	Normal	Crash
a	(1, 2)	—	16	8	2,000	4,400
b	(1, 3)	—	14	9	1,000	1,800
c	(2, 4)	a	8	6	500	700
d	(2, 5)	a	5	4	600	1,300
e	(3, 5)	b	4	2	1,500	3,000
f	(3, 6)	b	6	4	800	1,600
g	(4, 6)	c	10	7	3,000	4,500
h	(5, 6)	d, e	15	10	5,000	8,000

a. Construct the project network.

b. Manually crash the network to 28 weeks.

c. Formulate the general linear programming model for this network.

d. Formulate the linear programming crashing model that would crash this model by the maximum amount.

28. Formulate the general linear programming model for problem 4, and solve using the computer.

29. Formulate the general linear programming model for the project network for installing an order processing system shown in Figure 13, and solve using the computer.

30. For the example problem at the end of this chapter, assume that the most likely times (m) are the normal activity times and the optimistic times (a) are the activity crash times. Further assume that the activities have the following normal and crash costs.

Activity	Costs (normal cost, crash cost)
1 → 2	($100, 400)
1 → 3	($250, 400)
2 → 3	($400, 800)
2 → 4	($200, 400)
3 → 4	($150, 300)
3 → 5	($100, 100)
4 → 5	($300, 500)

   a. Formulate the general linear programming model for this project network using expected activity times (t).

   b. Formulate the linear programming crashing model that would crash this network by the maximum amount.

   c. Solve this model using the computer.

31. The following table provides the crash data for the network project described in problem 12. The normal activity times are considered to be deterministic and not probabilistic. Using the computer, crash the network to 26 weeks. Indicate how much it would cost the bank, and then indicate the critical path.

Activity	Activity Time (weeks) Normal	Crash	Activity Cost ($) Normal	Crash
a	9	7	4,800	6,300
b	11	9	9,100	15,500
c	7	5	3,000	4,000
d	10	8	3,600	5,000
e	1	1	0	0
f	5	3	1,500	2,000
g	6	5	1,800	2,000
h	3	3	0	0
i	1	1	0	0
j	2	2	0	0
k	8	6	5,000	7,000

32. The following table provides the crash data for the network project described in problem 6. Using the computer, crash the network to 32 months. Indicate the first critical path activities and then the cost of crashing the network.

Activity	Activity Time (months)		Activity Cost ($1,000s)	
	Normal	Crash	Normal	Crash
1 → 2	8	5	700	1,200
1 → 3	10	9	1,600	2,000
1 → 4	9	7	900	1,500
2 → 5	6	3	500	900
2 → 6	4	2	500	700
3 → 5	5	4	500	800
4 → 5	0	0	0	0
4 → 7	7	5	700	1,000
5 → 7	12	10	1,800	2,300
5 → 8	15	12	1,400	2,000
6 → 9	18	14	1,400	3,200
7 → 8	4	3	500	800
8 → 9	7	6	800	1,400

■ CASE PROBLEM

THE BLOODLESS COUP CONCERT

John Aaron called the meeting of the Programs and Arts Committee of the Student Government Association to order. "Okay, okay, everybody, quiet down. I have an important announcement to make," he shouted above the noise. The room got quiet and John started again, "Well, you guys, we can have the Coup."

His audience looked puzzled, and Randy Jones asked, "What coup have we scored this time, John?"

"The Coup, the Coup! You know, the rock group, the Bloodless Coup!"

Everyone in the room cheered and started talking excitedly. John stood up and waved his arms and shouted, "Hey, calm down, everybody, and listen up." The room quieted again and everyone focused on John. "The good news is that they can come." He paused a moment. "The bad news is that they will be here in 18 days."

The students groaned and seemed to share Jim Hastings' feelings. "No way, man. It can't be done. Why can't we put it off for a couple of weeks?"

John answered, "They're just starting their new tour and are looking for some warm-up concerts. They'll be traveling near here for their first concert date in D.C. and saw they had a letter from us, so they said they could come now. But that's it, now or never." He looked around the room at the solemn faces. "Look, you guys, we can handle this. Let's think of what we have to do. Come on, perk up. Let's make a list of everything we have to do to get ready and figure out how long it will take. So somebody tell me what we have to do first!"

Anna Mendoza shouted from the back of the room, "We have to find a place; you know, get an auditorium somewhere. I've done that before, and it should take anywhere from two days up to seven days, most likely about four days."

"Okay, that's great," John said, as he wrote down the activity "Secure auditorium" on the blackboard, with the times out to the side. "What's next?"

"We need to print tickets—and quick," Tracey Shea called. "It could only take a day if the printer isn't busy, but it could take up to four days if he is. It should probably take about two days."

"But we can't print tickets until we know where the concert will be, because of the security arrangement," Andy Taylor noted.

"Right," said John. "Get the auditorium first; then print the tickets. What else?"

"We need to make hotel and transportation arrangements for the Coup and their entourage while they're here," Jim Hastings proposed. "But we better not do that until we get the auditorium. If we can't find a place for the concert, everything falls through."

"How long do you think it will take to make the arrangements?" John asked.

"Oh, between three and ten days, probably about five, most likely," Jim answered.

"We also have to negotiate with the local union for concert employees, stagehands, and whoever else we need to hire," Reggie Wilkes interjected. "That could take a day or up to eight days, but three days would be my best guess."

"We should probably also hold off on talking to the union until we get the auditorium," John added. "That will probably be a factor in the negotiations."

"After we work things out with the union, we can hire some stagehands," Reggie continued. "That could take as few as two days but as long as seven. I imagine it'll take about four days. We should also be able to get some student ushers at the same time, once we get union approval. That could take only a day, but it has taken five days in the past; three days is probably the most likely."

"We need to arrange a press conference," said Art Cohen, who was leaning against a wall. "This is a heavy group, big time."

"But doesn't a press conference usually take place at the hotel?" John asked.

"Yeah, that's right," Art answered. "We can't make arrangements for the press conference until we work things out with the hotel. When we do that, it should take about three days to set up a press conference—two days if we're lucky and four at the most."

The room got quiet as everyone thought.

"What else?" John asked.

"Hey, I know," Annie Roark spoke up. "Once we hire the stagehands, they have to set up the stage. I think that could be done in a couple of days, but it could take up to six days, with three most likely." She paused for a moment before adding, "And we can also assign the ushers to their jobs once we hire them. That shouldn't take long, maybe only a day—three days worst, probably two days would be a good time to put down."

"We also have to do some advertising and promotion if we want people to show up for this thing," mentioned Art nonchalantly. "I guess we need to wait until we print the tickets, so we'll have something to sell. That depends on the media, the paper, and radio stations. I've worked with this before. It could get done really quick, like two days, if we can make the right contacts. But it

could take a lot longer, like twelve days if we hit any snags. We probably ought to count on six days as our best estimate."

"Hey, if we're going to promote this, shouldn't we also have a preliminary act, some other group?" Annie asked.

"Wow, I forgot all about that!" John exclaimed. "Hiring another act will take me between four and eight days; I can probably do it in five. I can start on that right away, at the same time you guys are arranging for an auditorium." He thought for a moment. "But we really can't begin to work on the promotion until I get the lead-in group. So what's left?"

"Sell the tickets," shouted several people at once.

"Right," said John. "We have to wait until they're printed; but I don't think we have to wait for the advertising and promotion to start, do we?"

"No," Jim replied. "But we should hire the preliminary act first so people will know what they're buying a ticket for."

"Agreed," said John. "The tickets could go quick; I suppose in the first day."

"Or," interrupted Mike Eggleston, "it could take longer. I remember two years ago, it took twelve days to sell out for the Cosmic Modem."

"Okay, so it's between one and twelve days to sell the tickets," said John, "but I think about five days is more likely. Everybody agree?"

The group nodded in unison and they all turned at once to the list of activities and times John had written on the blackboard.

Use PERT analysis to determine the probability that the concert preparations will be completed in time.

MOORE HOUSING CONTRACTORS

Moore Housing Contractors is negotiating a deal with Countryside Realtors to build six houses in a new development. Countryside wants Moore Contractors to start in late winter or early spring when the weather begins to moderate, and build on through the summer into the fall. The summer months are an especially busy time for the realty company, and it believes it can sell the houses almost as soon as they are ready, and sometimes even before. The houses all have similar floor plans and are of approximately equal size; only the exteriors are noticeably different. The completion time is so critical for Countryside Realtors that it is insisting that a project management network accompany the contractor's bid for the job with an estimate of the completion time for a house. The realtor also needs to be able to plan its offerings and marketing for the summer. It wants each

house to be completed within 45 days after it is started. If a house is not completed within this time frame it wants to be able to charge the contractor a penalty. Mary and Sandy Moore, the president and vice president, respectively, of Moore Contractors, are concerned about the prospect of a penalty charge. They want to be very confident that they can meet the deadline for a house before they enter into any kind of agreement with a penalty involved. (If there is a reasonable likelihood that they cannot finish a house within 45 days they want to increase their bid to cover potential penalty charges.)

The Moores are experienced home builders, so it was not difficult for them to list the activities involved in building a house or to estimate activity times. However, they made their estimates conservatively and tended to increase their pessimistic estimates to compensate for the possibility of bad weather and variations in their workforce. Following is a list of the activities involved in building a house and the activity time estimates.

Activity	Activity Description	Predecessors	Time (Days)		
			a	m	b
a	Excavation, pour footers	—	3	4	6
b	Lay foundation	a	2	3	5
c	Frame and roof	b	2	4	5
d	Lay drain tiles	b	1	2	4
e	Sewer (floor) drains	b	1	2	3
f	Install insulation	c	2	4	5
g	Pour basement floor	e	2	3	5
h	Rough plumbing, pipes	e	2	4	7
i	Install windows	f	1	3	4
j	Rough electrical wiring	f	1	2	4
k	Install furnace, air conditioner	c, g	3	5	8
l	Exterior brickwork	i	5	6	10
m	Install plasterboard, mud, plaster	j, h, k	6	8	12
n	Roof shingles, flashing	l	2	3	6
o	Attach gutter, downspouts	n	1	2	5
p	Grading	d, o	2	3	7
q	Lay subflooring	m	3	4	6
r	Lay driveway, walks, landscape	p	4	6	10
s	Finish carpentry	q	3	5	12
t	Kitchen cabinetry, sink, and appliances	q	2	4	8
u	Bathroom cabinetry, fixtures	q	2	3	6
v	Painting (interior and exterior)	t, u	4	6	10
w	Finish wood floors, lay carpet	v, s	2	5	8
x	Final electrical, light fixtures	v	1	3	4

A. Develop a CPM/PERT network for Moore Contractors and determine the probability that the company can complete a house within 45 days. Does it appear that the Moores might need to increase their bid to compensate for potential penalties?

B. Indicate which project activities Moore Contractors should be particularly diligent to keep on schedule by making sure workers and materials are always available. Also indicate which activities the company might shift workers from as the need arises.

Solutions to Selected Odd-Numbered Problems

1. 1–2–4 = 8, 1–3–4 = 10

3. 1–2–4–6 = 14, 1–2–4–5–6 = 23, 1–2–5–6 = 13, 1–3–5–6 = 22, 1–3–6 = 12

5. 1–2: $ES = 0$, $EF = 7$, $LS = 2$, $LF = 2$, $S = 2$; 1–3: $ES = 0$, $EF = 10$, $LS = 0$, $LF = 10$, $S = 0$; 2–4: $ES = 7$, $EF = 13$, $LS = 9$, $LF = 15$, $S = 2$; 3–4: $ES = 10$, $EF = 15$, $LS = 10$, $LF = 15$, $S = 0$; 3–5: $ES = 10$, $EF = 14$, $LS = 14$, $LF = 18$, $S = 4$; 4–5: $ES = 15$, $EF = 18$, $LS = 15$, $LF = 18$, $S = 0$; 5–6: $ES = 18$, $EF = 20$, $LS = 18$, $LF = 20$, $S = 0$; 1–3–4–5–6 = 20

7. 1–2: $ES = 0$, $EF = 10$, $LS = 0$, $LF = 0$, $S = 0$; 1–3: $ES = 0$, $EF = 7$, $LS = 5$, $LF = 12$, $S = 5$; 2–4: $ES = 10$, $EF = 14$, $LS = 14$, $LF = 18$, $S = 4$; 2–6: $ES = 10$, $EF = 25$, $LS = 10$, $LF = 25$, $S = 0$; 3–4: $ES = 7$, $EF = 13$, $LS = 12$, $LF = 18$, $S = 5$; 3–5: $ES = 7$, $EF = 19$, $LS = 13$, $LF = 25$, $S = 6$; 4–5: $ES = 14$, $EF = 18$, $LS = 21$, $LF = 25$, $S = 7$; 4–6: $ES = 14$, $EF = 21$, $LS = 18$, $LF = 25$, $S = 4$; 5–6: $ES = 19$, $EF = 19$, $LS = 25$, $LF = 25$, $S = 6$; 6–7: $ES = 25$, $EF = 34$, $LS = 25$, $LF = 34$, $S = 0$; 1–2–6–7 = 34

9. 1–3–6–10–11–14–15 = 78 weeks

11. 1–2–5–7 = 40.33, $\sigma = 5.95$

13. (e) 1–3–5–7–8–9; (f) $\mu = 46$ months, $\sigma = 5$ months

15. $P(x \geq 50) = .2119$

17. c–d–f–g–j–k–o–r = 160.83 min; $P(x \leq 180) = .9875$

19. $P(x \leq 15) = .0643$

21. a–b–d–j–n–o, $\mu = 45$ weeks, $\sigma = 4.1$ weeks, 50.3 weeks

23. a–e–f–g–j–o–p = 91.667, $\sigma = 3.308$, $P(x \leq 101) = .9976$

25. a–h–l–m–n–o–s–w; $\mu = 126.67$ days, $\sigma = 8.14$ days; $P(x \leq 150) = .9979$

27. (c) min. $Z = x_6$; s.t. $x_2 - x_1 \geq 16$, $x_3 - x_1 \geq 14$, $x_4 - x_2 \geq 8$, $x_5 - x_2 \geq 5$, $x_5 - x_3 \geq 4$, $x_6 - x_3 \geq 6$, $x_6 - x_4 \geq 10$, $x_6 - x_5 \geq 15$, $x_1 x_j \geq 0$

29. min. $Z = x_9$; s.t. $x_2 - x_1 \geq 8$, $x_3 - x_1 \geq 6$, $x_4 - x_1 \geq 3$, $x_5 - x_2 \geq 0$, $x_6 - x_2 \geq 5$, $x_5 - x_3 \geq 3$, $x_5 - x_4 \geq 4$, $x_7 - x_5 \geq 7$, $x_7 - x_8 \geq 0$, $x_8 - x_5 \geq 4$, $x_8 - x_4 \geq 2$, $x_9 - x_6 \geq 4$, $x_9 - x_7 \geq 9$, $x_i x_j \geq 0$; $x_1 = 0$, $x_2 = 9$, $x_3 = 6$, $x_4 = 3$, $x_5 = 9$, $x_6 = 14$, $x_7 = 16$, $x_8 = 16$, $x_9 = 25$

31. 1–2–4–5–8–9; crash cost = $5,100; total network cost = $33,900